Remnants of a Quiet Life

Henry Harris

Remnants of a Quiet Life

Henry Harris

Twin Serpents Limited
Oxford, UK

Published by Twin Serpents Limited 2006

10 digit ISBN 1–905524–26–9 (Paperback)
10 digit ISBN 1–905524–27–7 (Hardback)

13 digit ISBN 978–1–905524–26–6 (Paperback)
13 digit ISBN 978–1–905524–27–3 (Hardback)

Direct all enquiries through:

www.twinserpents.com

PUBLISHER'S PREFACE

Oxford University is not only seen as one of the great universities of the world, a national treasure, and somewhere that some of the best and brightest from many countries wish to study. It is also frequently considered remote, aloof, inaccessible, and populated by people as far removed from real life and common experiences as it is possible to be. It is true that its ways are old and its traditions sometimes a little incongruent with aspects of modern life and passing trends. However, like other similar institutions, it is one built of and defined by its members, and its enduring qualities – as well as its weaknesses – derive wholly from the human beings who are its members and custodians. This book, written by one of its longest-serving and most respected members, and at the same time one of the most significant scientists of his generation, reveals much of the humanity and heart which are so essential and integral to its vitality and strength. It provides a rare window into the life, perspectives, and experiences of the academic life, and thus affords an indirect view of the deeper nature of university life and of the University of which the author will forever be a part.

PREFACE

These tales, written in the unfettered years that followed my long tenure of a professorship at Oxford, reflect the experiences of an academic lifetime. With the exception of the narrator and a few, mainly historical, individuals mentioned by name, all the characters are fictional; but I like to think that these figments of my imagination might nonetheless afford a glimpse of what lies at the heart of academic life, at least as one man lived it.

Henry Harris
Oxford
Spring 2006

CONTENTS

CHAPTER 1

THE ANATOMY LESSON

The laboratory is set back from the road and partly screened by trees and shrubs. You do not see the full symmetry of the building until you pass through the wrought iron gates, painted a sober black, with ornamental flourishes tricked out in gold leaf. Then it towers above you, three storeys of dark red brick, decorated, but with restraint, in a Queen Anne style. Between it and the road there are garden beds stocked in summer with intricate patterns of bright flowers. Two stone staircases, with banisters also painted in black and gold, spiral up to the front doorway. I've climbed those stairs each working day for the best part of my life, and now, as I approach them, I seem always to pause for a moment to cast an affectionate eye on this gentle place, lit up by the morning sun or wistful in the rain.

Once inside the front doors, you find yourself in a hall with walls of blue-veined marble. Three marble steps lead up to a great oak staircase, which is also a spiral, but rectangular, hugging the line of the walls. On one side of it, there is an elaborately carved banister, on the other, oak panelling to match. Above the panelling, portraits of my predecessors look out into nothingness, ageing professors, all distinguished in their time, one or two perhaps distinguished for all time. My predecessors must have trudged up that staircase each day much as I now do; I can still hear the heavy tread of the last of them. The long top corridor, punctuated at regular intervals by heavy wooden doors with brass handles, tunnels through a series of plasterwork arches and finally comes to a stop at an even more impressive door which, for more than a quarter of a century, has had my name on it.

Nothing about the grand entrance or the graceful corridor betrays the nature of the activity that goes on behind the doors with brass handles. It is only when you turn a handle and enter one of the rooms that the dense array of scientific equipment tells you what we are about. If you knew nothing about the building or the monumental advances in medical science that had taken place there, you might have taken it for an art gallery; the contents of the rooms would have come as a surprise. But not the room with my name on the door. That was designed in an age when professors were taken seriously. In the architect's plan, it is referred to as a study, not an office. The walls are panelled and lined with bookshelves; there is a great Edwardian desk that sits solidly in the middle of an expanse of green carpet and, in the corner, a fireplace with a marble surround. French windows open on to a small balcony and look out over the trees and lawns of the university parks. The view from that window, changing as the seasons come and go, is one of the subtle threads that bind me to this place.

Usually my secretary has sorted the mail before I arrive, but this morning I have beaten her to it and taken the thick bundle of unopened envelopes up to my desk. They are almost always brown or white. It's rare for anything of interest to come in a brown envelope. Most of them contain circulars, questionnaires, items of unwanted information or directives of various kinds from the university bureaucracy. Nothing that comes from that source does much to enhance the intellectual life of this laboratory. I flip through the brown envelopes and begin with one marked "Personal and Confidential". It contains a circular informing me that the date of a meeting, which is itself neither personal nor confidential, has been changed. I slit open another. It contains a piece of legitimised fatuity from the university safety office. A third offers me a report of a sub-committee, thought by some to be important. Its principal conclusion is that although a number of steps that might be taken are highly desirable, none is possible in the "present climate of financial stringency". More than half of what the brown envelopes bring ends up in my waste paper basket. Most of what's left is filed unanswered and is never again consulted. I pass a few items on to my administrator. He is not exactly overjoyed at receiving them, but he is an old hand at minimally brief replies.

The white envelopes are sometimes more interesting. I open one with an elaborate crest, the coat of arms of an obscure, but richly endowed, American university. The dean is asking for my assessment of a man whom they are considering for a professorship. His enquiry has a highly stylised format. Is the man in the top 1% of those working in his area? The top 10%? Is his work of outstanding originality? Does he have powerful administrative skills? Is he an inspired teacher? I pick up my tape recorder and wearily tell the dean that the man in question has none of these attributes but that, in my view, he would nonetheless more than adequately fill the post for which he was being considered.

There are two letters from former students asking me whether I would be willing to write references to support their applications for jobs. I do my best for them, this side of perjury. The next letter tells me that someone is organising a conference on my subject in Erice. Would I give the opening lecture? Why Erice? Because an Italian scientist of aristocratic Sicilian origins once thought that it would be good for Sicily to have an international conference centre and decided that the hill village of Erice was the place to put it. There are too many conferences and I've been to Erice. I explain that I'm already committed to another engagement on those particular dates.

There is only one letter that has any scientific content. This comes from Fritz Lipmann, one of the most eminent biochemists of his day. Fritz, now in his eighties, writes to tell me that a recent paper of mine has given him an idea which he expounds in three tightly written pages. I'll answer that letter by hand later in the day. And finally there's an assortment of items whose very envelopes announce that they are peddling something: journals, books, scientific equipment, insurance, financial services, even wines at reduced prices. All these go unopened to my waste paper basket.

I take the completed tape in to my secretary and return to my room to look at the day's crop of scientific journals. It's a lean day; there are only three of them. I scour the contents of the first two but find nothing of much interest to me. The third is *Nature*, that weekly pot-pourri of the science that's in the news. The highlight of this week's issue is a group of three papers, each having half-a-dozen or more authors and all saying the same thing. I marvel at the change in scientific style that has taken place in my lifetime. My mentors would have advised me that if all I could think of doing was the

13

obvious thing that others were also about to do, I would be better off selling shirts. Yet here are three large groups, all doing the same obvious thing, fully aware of each other's presence and content nonetheless to race for the only prize at stake: beating one's competitors into print. What a disappointment it must be for the winners to find that the editor has ignored the marginally different dates on which the papers were submitted and decided to publish them together. It is a constant source of pleasure to me that in this laboratory science continues to be done in an older tradition.

Three people have asked to see me this morning. My administrator is having some trouble with one of the technicians who is having a tantrum. What action should he take? The head of the workshop has come upon an unforeseen snag in one of the laboratory rooms that they are refurbishing. One of the younger scientists says he needs a rather expensive piece of equipment that we don't have. By the time I've spoken to the three of them it is 10.30. Apart from looking at the journals, which is my daily exercise in continuing education, everything I've done since I got in comes under the general heading of administration. I do it each morning in much the same way as I brush my teeth, without enthusiasm but acknowledging that it is necessary. My day begins when, finally, I open the door that leads from my study into my laboratory.

The sudden transition reiterates the contrast between the external appearance of the building and its function: the study is an Edwardian scholar's haven but the laboratory is, inevitably, a clutter of surrealist instrumentation softened, but only slightly, by cupboards and benches still made of wood and huge windows which, like those in my study, look out over the university parks. I am investigating a group of genes that I stumbled upon many years ago and that are now the centre of a great deal of attention. These are normal genes that have the ability to suppress the malignant characteristics of cancer cells. It is not difficult to see why they should be of interest. I am trying to isolate them and find out how they work. The experiment I have in hand is one in which fragments of chromosomes containing these genes have been introduced into some cancer cells, and I am waiting to see what happens. Waiting is nine-tenths of research.

The cells are grown in small transparent plastic flasks that you can

14

examine under the microscope. They are half-filled with a salmon pink fluid and don't look unattractive when they are lined up on a bench. Botanists are more fortunate; they can work with orchids if they choose. I take one of the flasks to a microscope and examine the cells in it. I have worked with them for years and know them like the back of my hand. Here and there I find a cell that has undergone an interesting change in shape. That looks hopeful. But as I scan the flask I notice that in one corner there is a small tangle of very fine filaments that I recognise at once as a mould. From time to time spores dispersed into the air by moulds find their way into the flasks and germinate there. Flasks contaminated in this way usually have to be discarded, as it's extremely difficult to remove the mould completely. If spores have got into the solutions that are used to make up the salmon pink culture fluid, then most of the flasks will be contaminated. I scan a few more flasks and find wisps of mould in all of them. The experiment will have to be scrapped. A week's work down the drain. My technician, who has been with me for years, knows that we shall have to start all over again. A little despondently she drops the pink flasks into the waste disposal bin and then removes from the refrigerator the solutions we have been using. They will all need to be made up afresh and the sterility of our procedures checked. It will be a couple of days before we can start again. If you choose research as a career, disappointment will be your daily bread. You'd better get used to it.

Along the corridor two laboratory rooms are occupied by my Ph.D. students. There are four, two men and two women, all working on different aspects of the same central problem: how normal genes suppress the malignant characteristics of cancer cells. Each of them is examining this question in a different way, and in a different kind of cell. I like to talk to them every few days, partly to see how their work is going and partly because I enjoy their company. As there's nothing much for me to do in my own laboratory for the time being, I take the opportunity to go and see whether they are having any better luck.

One of the young men is an American, the scion of one of the founding families of a legendary city in the Deep South. He had been educated at Harvard, but you can still hear the South in his voice. He is extremely courteous, perhaps excessively so. He is sitting at his desk reading a journal, but as I enter the room he drops it and gets up with a smile that gives me the impression that he's pleased to see me. My visits are not always welcome, although I make a point of withdrawing immediately if the person I want to see is in the middle of some experimental manipulation. A couple of weeks earlier he had lent me W. J. Cash's *The Mind of the South* which I had not previously read. So we begin with *The Mind of the South*. Does he share Cash's view of it? His reply is full of ambiguities and reservations, the natural product of a Harvard education superimposed on a Southern childhood. We move only gradually to his experimental work. He has been stuck for some time over a technical difficulty that should in principle be readily soluble, but he seems to be making very heavy weather of it. I am able to offer a couple of suggestions; some years previously, in another context, I had been faced with a similar difficulty. The other aspiring Ph.D. in that room is a Cambridge graduate who is, in almost every respect, the antithesis of the Southern Gentleman. His long black hair is always unkempt and he has a straggly beard. He was the top student in his year at Cambridge, but seems determined not to let it show. He consciously exaggerates his native Yorkshire accent, and laces his speech with as many plebeian expletives as it will bear. Nothing upper-class is going to rub off on him. He is standing in the far corner of the room with his back to me, fiddling with a piece of apparatus. He is, or pretends to be, engrossed in what he is doing. I let him be.

The two girls next door also make an interesting contrast. One is extremely diffident and hesitates to show me her results for fear that I might find them short of perfect. In fact, she is the most gifted of my present crop of graduate students and her work is always meticulous. She is a little less diffident this morning and shows me some graphs that decisively prove a point that she has been making to me for some time but that I have been rather reluctant to accept. Her companion is a self-consciously pretty girl, always dressed and made up as if she were going out to dinner. She has her eye on the Southern Gentleman. I have the impression that she does not stop to think about what she is doing, but she somehow manages nonetheless to ferret out bits of useful information. She wants me to see some photographs she has taken. They show cells multiplying vigorously under conditions that would not normally support their growth. This might well be an important observation, but the photographs are awful. I suggest that she repeat the experiment and ask our photographer to help her with the next lot of photographs.

It's almost half-past-twelve by the time I finish with the Ph.D. students. I usually have lunch in the graduate club over the road. The food is tedious, but it's close by and the club is a good place to pick up gossip. I put on my jacket and make my way down the great oak staircase, conscious, as always, of the stern gaze of my predecessors. Most of the people who enter the building through the front doorway are not difficult to identify. The undergraduates come in a great wave, a few minutes before, or a few minutes after, their lecture is due to begin. In the 1960s they wore a uniform of sandals, blue jeans, and floral shirts; in the 1970s we had a resurgence of dandyism, and now there's a confused mixture of the two modes. Commercial travellers always appear in smart suits and carry briefcases; if they are women, they wear a lot of make-up. Scientists from other laboratories, in their working clothes naturally, know exactly where they want to go. Overseas visitors seem a little lost. The plumber wears a cloth cap and carries his bag of tools.

But I have never seen anything like the apparition that confronts me in the hall this time. He is a very big man, well into his seventies I should say; even with the stoop of old age he towers over me. His great round head is completely bald with ears that jut out at right angles. The sun and the wind have obviously long used his face as an anvil, the leathery skin is incised with a network of fine lines and dotted with small warts. His hands match his face: huge rugged objects with prominent veins and broken fingernails. You can see at a glance that he has spent his life working out of doors, and there's something about him that suggests a farm rather than a building site. He is wearing a well-worn charcoal-grey three piece suit of very conservative cut, obviously his Sunday best. The trousers are a little short and reveal a pair of heavy black lace-up boots. In one hand he has a plastic carrier bag on which orange letters tell the world that good food costs less at Sainsbury's. I suspect that it contains his lunch. He is sweating profusely and mops his forehead with a large, originally white, handkerchief as he approaches me.

"Excuse me, sir" he says, and I shall not attempt to mimic the flat

17

vowels and burred 'r's of his undiluted Gloucestershire speech. "Excuse me, sir" he repeats, "I wonder if you could help me? I want to leave my body for medical research."

I sometimes get letters from people who want to do this and redirect them to the appropriate place, but I've never had it sprung on me at our front door. When I tell him that ours isn't the right department, he almost bursts into tears, and then the whole story comes pouring out. He has already been to the hospital, which is three miles out of town, and from there has been misdirected to two other laboratories. We were his last hope. I calm him down and tell him that the Department of Anatomy is where he ought to go, that it's only a couple of hundred yards up the road, and that I'll take him there myself. This produces a great gush of relief and gratitude. I settle him in the library while I make a telephone call to Anatomy. I tell the professor's secretary that I'm bringing them a customer and that they must treat him as a VIP; a cup of tea would help.

As we walk across to Anatomy, he explains how it came about that he decided to leave his body for medical research. He is, as I guessed, a farm labourer and has spent the whole of his life working on farms in the surrounding region. About a year ago he fell from a combine harvester and broke his ankle. It was a complicated fracture that kept him in hospital for almost three weeks. He was amazed at the attention that was showered upon him, especially the attention of the nurses, and although his ankle is still a bit tender, he assures me that he is now as right as rain. When he left hospital, he very much wanted to do something to repay the kindness he had received, but he had no money and couldn't think of anything he could do. Then it struck him that he did have one possession that might be useful – his body. He had heard of people bequeathing their bodies for medical research and he decided that that was what he was going to do. He had spent the whole of the morning trying in vain to implement his decision. He is still enmeshed in the details of the morning's frustrations when we reach the Anatomy building. The secretary is at the front entrance waiting for us. She at once offers him some tea and asks him whether he would like something to eat. He is very glad to have the tea, but confides that he has his own lunch with him and holds up the Sainsbury's carrier bag as evidence. There's nothing more for me to do. I wish the old man a long life, shake his hand, and wander off to the faculty club. Over lunch the only gossip I pick up is that the safety office is about to appoint yet another member of staff.

This afternoon we have a meeting of the Faculty Board. I am in two minds about whether I should go. One of my predecessors did not attend a single meeting for more than ten years. It didn't seem to have made much difference to anything that mattered. The main item on the menu for today is a report of a committee set up to review the curriculum. For as long as I can remember there has never been a time when some part of the curriculum wasn't being reviewed. It is difficult to see what, if anything, these reviews achieve. The good students assimilate what they are interested in without effort and what they are not interested in without much effort. They are not bound by the curriculum and would achieve much the same standard however eccentric the curriculum might be. The bad students make a hash of whatever they're asked to do. Those that are neither good nor bad remain neither good nor bad. Nonethless, there is nothing that engenders as much heat as a review of the curriculum. One might have thought that rational self-interest would induce dons to seek to reduce their teaching burden so that there would always be room to spare in the curriculum. The reverse seems to be the case. Most of them appear to be totally convinced of the overriding importance of their own specialty and, surprising as it may seem, actually seek to expand its representation in the curriculum. The end result is that, despite endless and often ill-tempered discussions, curricular problems are never solved, they are merely modified. There is therefore more than enough inducement for me to avoid the meeting this afternoon. But I go nonetheless. There's a ticklish item involving one of the lecturers in our department and I feel that I should give him my support.

The meeting drags on as I expected it would. The chairman is not in control and has no talent for avoiding diversions or gagging the loquacious. There are a couple of licensed pedants who insist on making an issue of principle out of every trivium. When a point appears at last to be agreed, one or other of them will reopen the question. The same ground is covered again and again. Finally, a patently unsatisfactory compromise is reached, and we flounder on to the next item. Tempers fray a little. A lecturer from one of the departments with industrial connections has applied for unscheduled leave of absence in order to do a piece of research in a large industrial laboratory. The case rests on access to facilities that are not available in the lecturer's own department and on the indirect benefits to the department that are likely to flow from the arrangement. The application is strongly opposed by two individuals who have never been consulted by industry in their lives. A compromise is again grudgingly agreed: the lecturer is granted his leave of absence but for a substantially shorter period than he needs.

There is a clutch of appointments to be made to various committees. The difficulty here is that the people who ought to be sitting on these committees are reluctant to do so, because the surfeit of committees deflects them from the academic work which is their essential function. It would be in everybody's interest if the people who are eager to sit on committees were not permitted to do so, but, for one reason or another, they always seem to end up there nonetheless. That might be why the world is how it is. After a couple of hours people begin to drift away, more from boredom or frustration than because they have some pressing appointment. I have to stay on because the item involving the lecturer from our department is close to the end of the agenda. Perhaps because even the aficionados of faculty board meetings are now almost at the end of their tether, the matter is quickly and satisfactorily resolved. If you are in the business of preparing agendas and have a controversial item, put it at the end of a long meeting.

By the time I get back to the laboratory the afternoon has been blown away. It's too late to start anything much, so I decide to have a word with the scientists from overseas who are working with me this year. There are three of them. One is the chairman of the department of biochemistry in a large Midwestern university. He is a distinguished man, but it is many years since he has been anywhere near an experiment. When he wrote to ask me whether I could take him for a sabbatical year, he expressed the hope that he might be able to get back to doing a little research with his own hands. I was rather sceptical, because it very rarely happens that a scientist who has distanced himself from experimental work for any length of time can return to it. I was therefore surprised, and delighted, to find

20

that he was one of the rare exceptions. He isn't doing anything too revolutionary, but whenever I enter his laboratory he is hard at it and as happy as a sand-boy. He never wears a white coat, so I can always admire the large dishcloth that hangs habitually from his hip pocket. But this afternoon he has already gone home, and I am greeted by a young Swede who shares the laboratory with him. This is a very serious young man who has some difficulty in coping with a famous father. He works obsessionally, as if his life depended on it. He is endeavouring to determine the precise location of one of the genes we are interested in. He shows me the results he has accumulated since last I spoke to him. They are very impressive. I am confident that he will succeed in locating that gene, and that the evidence will be decisive. The third of my overseas visitors occupies a small room on the other side of the corridor, and he is still there when I open the door. He is a Frenchman who bears a name that is part of the history of France and whose interest in Proust is at least as passionate as his interest in science. He is a good scientist, but he has a tendency to believe that if nature isn't doing exactly as he expects, she's merely being difficult. He is studying the ways in which genes are put out of action in cancer cells, and I like to talk to him about his work because he always has an interesting slant on it. But today he prefers to talk about Proust. That suits me fine.

When I return to my study, I re-read the letter from Fritz Lipmann and then sit down to answer it. I take each point he raises and discuss it systematically. I know that if I were to omit one, I should at once get another letter asking about the point I had missed. By the time I've finished there are five handwritten pages. I am pleased to have taken the trouble to answer him at such length, as I don't know how many more letters I can expect to receive from Fritz. I can hear the chimes of the great bells echoing across the town. I fold the five pages into an airmail envelope, stick it down and address it. Then I gather my things, plod once more down the great staircase and hear the front door click shut behind me as I sniff the evening air. I drive home slowly through the half-congealed traffic. At the crossroads in the centre of town I am stopped by a traffic light. I look aimlessly out of my window at the people crowding the pavement, and there, unmistakable, I see him again, the old man who wanted to leave his body for medical research. He still has his carrier bag, though there doesn't seem to be anything in it now, and his face is wreathed in smiles.

CHAPTER 2

THE BRIDGE PLAYERS

My favourite place in college is the window sill in the corner of the room where we have coffee after lunch. I find the armchairs too soft and deep for coffee-drinking, but if I sit on the window sill I can not only take my coffee without strain but also talk to several people at the same time, for in that corner of the room the armchairs are so disposed that the window sill forms the centre of a manageable semicircle. None of our own philosophers having drifted into the semicircle that day, we were gossiping, unimpeded, about the personal characteristics of philosophers. We had done a pretty thorough hatchet job on three or four of them when one of the historians, looking at me with raised eyebrows, asked:

"Did you know Maurice T.?" And, as if the name were a cue for the next slide, a deceptively peaceful scene from another time and another place sprang to my mind: a small panelled room with portraits of disgruntled old men on its walls and, in the middle, an elaborately ugly Victorian card table at which Maurice T. sat staring glumly at his cards while his three companions exchanged glances. I had only the briefest glimpse of the card-players, for I had burst into the room unaware that a game of bridge was under way there and withdrew at once in a flurry of confused apologies. Perhaps it was my embarrassment that made the scene stick in my memory, but the picture was sharp, even after a lapse of twenty years, and, as it came back to me, it really was as if a slide had been projected onto my mind for a second or two and then briskly taken off.

I had been elected into a fellowship of that college a year or two previously, and Maurice was by a long stretch its most senior fellow. I didn't yet know that, after college feasts and domus nights,

23

Maurice liked to organize a serious game of bridge in that room and that the rest of us were expected not to disturb it. Maurice, Alan, Harvey and Paul. Bridge was the only thing that ever brought peace to those warring factions. Maurice, the philosopher, the sardonic critic who made mincemeat of any loose phrase that floated innocently in his direction; Alan, the experimental physicist who regarded research in the humanities as at best frivolous; Harvey, the voracious consumer of modern English literature who regarded the study of any other literature as a fall from grace and the study of language as pedantry; and Paul, the young classicist whose intellectual energies were then totally devoted to the study of language and for whom modern English literature was a moment of light relief at the weekends. They straddled the generations. Maurice was approaching retirement. He had been elected into his fellowship before the war and was one of the few pre-war dons still in post. Alan and Harvey were within sight of middle age, and Paul, elected immediately on graduation, still had the air of a schoolboy.

Paul was elected a little after me, so I was present at the meeting of the governing body that made the election. He had been a brilliant undergraduate – 'pure alpha' his referees had assured us. Although the post was a tutorial fellowship, which at that time was a job for life, and Paul had as yet published nothing, the selection committee were unanimous in recommending that we should snap him up. Alan, who had earlier argued against having a classicist at all and had urged that the funds be used to establish a tutorial fellowship in physical chemistry (fruitlessly, of course, for on the governing body the humanities far outweighed the sciences), now opposed the election. He made his case with the moral fervour of a fundamentalist preacher and, indeed, in another age that is what he might very well have been. His parents had both been school teachers in a small Yorkshire town, and I can imagine a childhood moulded in a discipline of uncompromising probity. Although the years had modified his speech, you could still hear the North in it, more marked, of course, when his emotions were engaged. When I first met him, it struck me how closely he conformed to my mental picture of Heathcliff – a dark, rugged face with bushy eyebrows and a mass of curly brown hair, greying now not at the temples, gracefully, but in a haphazard fashion rather like the bright flecks in a Donegal tweed. To elect a man into a permanent academic post on the strength of his prowess in undergraduate exercises was, in Alan's view, a scandal. I had heard that argument many times before, but Alan went too far. He talked as if the university were full of people who were elected at graduation and thereafter didn't write a single line, and he couldn't resist dragging in words like decadence and corruption. Maurice picked him clean, and Paul was duly elected. Alan did, in the end, learn how to get his way with a committee, but by the time he had acquired that skill, he no longer bore much resemblance to the Heathcliff that I remembered.

For Maurice, Alan's diatribe had been too near home for comfort. Maurice, too, had been elected to his fellowship on graduation and, apart from a single early article on Emile Meyerson, which to me revealed an almost total incomprehension of scientific practice, had since published nothing but a handful of ruthlessly destructive book reviews. Yet he was an extraordinarily intelligent man, held almost in awe by some of his philosophical colleagues. In the art of demolishing nonsense, I never met his equal – brilliantly witty, perceptive, and unanswerable. He lived a solitary life in college and seemed to have no circle of friends outside it. I think it would have been difficult to be a close friend of Maurice's, for he would have been unable to resist the impulse to take your words apart if, in an unguarded moment, you said something that was merely approximate. Maurice's conversational style always reminded me of a bird of prey, an impression that was curiously reinforced by his physical appearance. He was a tall angular man, so lean as to appear almost emaciated, and, in a certain light, you could almost discern the skull beneath the chiselled aquiline features. The only time I ever saw him indulging in what might pass for good natured banter was when I caught him setting off to play tennis with one of his pupils, and then, in shorts, he was more like an ibis than an eagle. He had a flat in London, although none of us knew exactly where, and he never gave us any inkling of what he did when, from time to time, he disappeared for a few days.

How did I come to read his early article on Meyerson? An old school friend of mine, a mathematician with a casual interest in scientific formalisms, had once delved a little into Meyerson, and when he heard that Maurice and I were at the same college, he sent me a photocopy of Maurice's otherwise surely forgotten piece. That gave me my chance to break the ice with Maurice. He was amazed that I should know of the existence of the article, to say nothing of my having read it. I told him that I had greatly enjoyed his dismantling of Meyerson's view of science (which was true), but that I had some pretty serious reservations about what he had put in its place. As we talked, it transpired that he had never set foot in a laboratory in his life. I complained that it was altogether unreasonable to expect to be able to write sensibly about science when you have never been exposed to the real thing, even in passing; and I argued that the attempts of philosophers to impose logical schemata on the intricate and deeply imaginative intellectual processes that generate science was futile.

Our conversation ended with my asking Maurice whether he would like to visit my laboratory some time to sample for himself the flavour of science in the making. To my surprise, Maurice accepted the invitation with alacrity, and that's how it came about that he spent the whole of one Friday wandering from room to room and talking to the young scientists about their work. I had asked him to come for mid-morning coffee, and I expected that he would have had enough in an hour or two; but when the morning was over, he asked whether he might come back later in the day, and then he stayed on until it was time to return to college for dinner. I never again heard him mock what he imagined to be the practice of science or make caustic comments about the dictatorial mentality of science professors.

It was rumoured that Maurice had for years been incubating a major work on Leibnitz. I always doubted whether, despite his great intelligence, he was capable of it. To begin with, he was no mathematician, and I did not see how you could hope to deal adequately with Leibnitz if you could not encompass his mathematical work. Even the broad generalisations that Leibnitz made about the nature of the universe, or the logical rules that he formulated, had their origins in mathematical ideas. An even more severe impediment in Maurice's case was a very imperfect knowledge of the German language. Like most Greats men, Maurice had a smattering of German and could certainly make himself understood when occasionally a summer holiday took him to the

Bavarian alps. But, even if his Latin was secure enough for the major works, I found it difficult to believe that he could cope efficiently with Leibnitz's seventeenth century German. It seemed to me that if that book on Leibnitz ever did appear, it wasn't going to be the definitive work that many expected. In fact, it never did appear, but for a deeper reason than either mathematical or linguistic insufficiency. Maurice wrote nothing in the last thirty years of his life essentially because he had lost faith in philosophy. I was by chance given a rare insight into the depth of his disenchantment. I had buttonholed him in the common room in the hope that he might be able to clarify for me what philosophers meant when they used the term 'necessary identity'. For a reason that is no longer interesting, I had become entangled in the confusion surrounding the use of the word 'identity' and, in particular, was at a loss to see how the much quoted criterion proposed by Leibnitz could ever be applied to material objects in the real world. With some reluctance, almost as if he didn't really believe what he was saying, Maurice rehearsed the traditional distinctions and then, in a tired voice, added:

"Don't get bogged down in philosophy, Henry. It doesn't lead anywhere."

Some months later Maurice buttonholed me. He made out that he had a close friend who had just been told that he had a cancer of the lung and that surgery was imperative. Maurice wanted to know in detail what the surgery would involve and what the chances of a complete cure were. One glance told me that the close friend didn't exist and that Maurice was asking about himself. I was, of course, in no position to give him the detailed information that he sought and don't know what he made of the generalities that I was able to offer. In any case, he must have decided that the odds were not short enough to warrant the trauma of surgery. Two days after we spoke, he was found dead in his bed. His body was cremated and, in accordance with his wishes, there was neither funeral nor memorial service. Bachelors who live their whole lives in college sometimes accumulate large sums of money, and we were rather surprised at the size of Maurice's estate. He made a small bequest to the college which he hoped would be used, at least in part, to buy books for the library, but the bulk of his fortune went to a small orphanage in Shropshire. None of us knew anything about his origins.

27

In physical appearance, Harvey was the direct antithesis of Maurice. If Maurice was a bird of prey, Harvey was a goose fattened for Christmas. Of less than average height and grossly overweight, he waddled about the college in a state of complete disarray, his sparse fair hair dishevelled, his grubby clothes straining to fulfil their intended function. He was a compulsive reader, and when he was not feeding or talking, he was always to be found with his nose in a modern novel or, much more rarely, in a newly published book of verse. He seemed to remember accurately a great deal of what he read, for often, in conversation, he would complete a lengthy quotation that someone else was struggling with, or, if some passage that he had read recently appealed to him, he could, if prompted, go on reciting it until we stopped him. I suppose he knew as much as any man about contemporary English fiction, but there was never any rumour that he was going to produce the definitive book on the subject, partly because the subject did not lend itself to a definitive book, and partly because he was one of those people who are much too busy taking in information to be able to distill it into a work of any great depth or originality. But he did, from time to time, produce an elegant, if slight, essay, and when there were enough of them he had them gathered together into a volume which received high praise from the reviewers.

I'm not sure that he was able to read French with ease, and he certainly didn't read it for pleasure. When, unexpectedly, he emitted a French phrase, the sounds he made might perhaps have meant something to an English schoolboy, but they wouldn't have meant much to a Frenchman. He did not seem to take the slightest interest in the literature of any other language, not even in translation. This circumscribed insularity was not, as I first imagined, due to Harvey's obvious difficulties with foreign languages; it was the expression of a firmly held belief that the literature of England was somehow on a higher plane than the literatures of other nations, deeper, more sensitive, more spiritual. To turn to other literatures was, in Harvey's view, to be deflected from the best to something demonstrably inferior. I found it difficult to believe that an educated man could genuinely hold such views and assumed, when Harvey let off this kind of steam, that he was simply adopting a pose. But I was disabused one evening at dinner when our mediaevalist brought in as his guest a renowned scholar from Italy who was then giving a series of lectures in London. It was at the time when widespread discussions were taking place in the university about the possibility of introducing joint honours schools in the humanities, so that undergraduates who wished to do so might read combinations of subjects such as philosophy with history or history with a modern language. Several interesting combinations had, in principle, already been agreed, but the Faculty of English Language and Literature stood aloof. It declined to combine with any other language, ancient or modern, or, indeed, with any other subject whatever.

Our Italian guest in all innocence asked Harvey, who sat at his side, to explain why this should be so. Unabashed, Harvey sprang to the defence of the English faculty's decision and presented a vigorous exposé of his own opinions. At first the visitor assumed that Harvey was indulging in some esoteric form of English humour and, with a broad smile, kept nodding his head in agreement; but as it dawned on him that Harvey was in deadly earnest, the smile turned slowly to goggle-eyed wonder. When, at last, Harvey had finished, the visitor drew a deep breath and then, in the gentlest of voices said: "The literature of England is the literature of an offshore island. It is an overt derivative of the literature of continental Europe and cannot be studied seriously except in that context." Harvey, white with suppressed anger, spluttered back: "And what about the English novel?" The visitor again paused for a moment before speaking, and then recited: "In France you have Balzac, Stendhal, Flaubert, Hugo, Proust, Gide, in Russia Gogol, Tolstoy, Dostoievski, Turgenev. Against these you set what? Dickens and Thackeray? Jane Austen and George Eliot?" And with that he turned away from Harvey and began to talk to the mediaevalist who had brought him in.

I was present at a similar passage of arms when the dinner guest, this time the head of another college, began to criticise the English faculty for having decided to reduce the English language component of the undergraduate curriculum to no more than an option; until then some study of the early English texts and the development of the language had been mandatory. "That was the only part of the course", he went on, "that stretched the undergraduate at all. If you take that out, all you have left is froth."

Harvey exploded. "You call the greatest literature in the world froth!" he exclaimed. "Those mediaeval texts are, and always were, dead boring, and it's simply an outrage to force young people to waste their time poring over linguistic minutiae that they're not interested in." At this point, Paul chipped in with a spirited defence of the intrinsic cultural value of the study of language, but Harvey went on and on until our guest, becoming impatient, allowed himself to say: "Well, Harvey, we shall have to agree to disagree. But I must say that, in my view, reading modern novels in your own language and talking about them simply isn't a serious intellectual discipline."

Harvey's dissolution as an academic was initiated by a Sunday newspaper. He had for years written book reviews for the little read magazines that give literary critics a chance to snipe at each other; occasionally a review for the Times Literary Supplement. For my taste, his reviews were a little too polished, not to say affected, but most critics regarded them as models of the genre. Then, one fateful day, Harvey was asked to review a group of three, as far as I could see, unrelated novels for one of the less toxic Sunday papers. He geared down, and produced a superficial, but quite amusing, twenty inches which must have been very well received for it was not long before we saw another exercise along the same lines. Before the year was out Harvey had become a regular Sunday feature and had graduated from book reviews to more general commentary on the literary scene. His column eventually carried a photograph of himself looking pensive.

Given his extraordinary memory and the immensity of his reading within the limits he set himself, we were not accustomed to Harvey making factual mistakes. But it was not long before these began to turn up in his Sunday pieces, and sometimes they were mistakes of a kind that would make a genuine scholar flush with shame. I suppose the pressure to meet a deadline each week inevitably engendered some degree of sloppiness, but the main trouble, it seemed to me, was that Harvey began to air his views on subjects that he knew nothing, or very little, about. I remember one occasion when he confused Stefan Zweig with Arnold Zweig, another when he attributed a famous novella by Heinrich Mann (it was a sensation in the 1930s as a film) to his brother Thomas. And his pronouncements became increasingly, almost laughably, parochial, much like the outlook of the paper for which he wrote.

The next Rubicon that Harvey crossed was his appearance on television. We were amazed to see him, all spruced up, his scruffy clothes replaced by what was meant to be an interesting Bohemian attire of very bright colours. He had been invited to join a panel of media luminaries who each week discussed two or three recently published books, usually novels. Since Harvey had consumed more English novels than anyone alive and could quote at length from most of them, he quickly became a star and was soon to be seen on all sorts of television programmes, whether they had anything to do with literature or not. He resigned his college fellowship many years before he was due to retire and moved to London where he appeared to live the semi-public life of a minor celebrity. By all accounts he thrived on it. Once, by chance, I saw him doing a TV commercial for a breakfast cereal.

I guessed that something curious was happening to Alan when he stopped deriding research in the humanities; and my guess was reinforced when I heard that he had agreed to serve on one of the college domestic committees that he had always previously scorned. We all knew that for Alan his experimental work came first, and he made no bones about declining obligations that he thought would deflect him seriously from it. He seemed to have achieved a substantial reputation in his field, for he was always flitting off to international conferences to give papers about his work, and every now and then he would bring into college some overseas visitor who had come to work with him. For some years he had been immersed in a complicated experiment that entailed the collation and analysis of measurements made by a number of laboratories in different parts of the world. Alan seemed to be at the centre of the collaboration, and we were told that the experiment would provide an answer to one of the most fundamental uncertainties about the nature of cosmic rays. In due course, two papers, of which Alan was the principal author, appeared together in a widely read journal accompanied by an editorial commentary which informed the reader that if the interpretation given to the data proved to be correct, the papers were a landmark. Alan couldn't suppress his excitement and, at the slightest provocation, would talk about his

31

work at length. He told me that what really counted was the interpretation of the data and that it was he who was primarily responsible for that. It was all rather beyond me, but I did hear another view of the work when I happened to share a compartment on the London train with one of the physics professors. He was, to my surprise, rather reserved about it all and hinted that he found Alan's interpretation rather far fetched. "I think we should wait a bit and see" he concluded.

We didn't have to wait long. A few months later, a densely mathematical paper appeared in the same journal and it took Alan apart. It was written by two distinguished theoretical physicists who claimed not only that Alan's interpretation didn't hold, but, much more serious, that the experiments as they had been designed couldn't in principle decide the issue at stake. I didn't have any occasion to speak to Alan for some weeks after that paper appeared and would in any case have avoided the subject, but I think it very probable that the profound change that took place in him over the next year or so had its origin in the complex algebra that brought about the collapse of his dreams.

His marriage, which had been under strain for some time, now broke up, and he began to take his meals in college much more frequently than before. It was, at first, a little incongruous to hear from his lips observations about the primacy of good undergraduate teaching, or the importance of pulling one's weight in the system. There are any number of committees in the university that nobody especially wants to sit on, and it was with some surprise that we noticed that Alan had become a member of three or four of them. He must have pulled his weight pretty vigorously, for it was not long before he became the chairman of two of them and was often to be seen scurrying to and from the central university offices. After a couple of years of this, he stood for election to the general board of the faculties and, by the narrowest of margins, made it. I gather he pulled his weight to good purpose there too and had no difficulty in finding his way onto the key subcommittees. But the most astonishing transformation of all was his apparent concern, often expressed publicly, that, in the crass utilitarian climate generated by one government after another, support for the humanities should not be allowed to wither away. Everything he said now was the essence of sweet reasonableness, and when, in due course, his hair went completely white, he acquired, more noticeably than anyone else in the higher ranks of the university administration, the air of an elder statesman.

There was, however, one small idiosyncrasy in the new style that I found particularly irritating. Whenever Alan rang me on a matter of university business, and, as far as I can remember, he never rang me about anything else, he always announced himself by some title and not by his name, even though we had known each other for years. "This is the chairman of such-and-such a committee speaking", he would say, the choice of title apparently determined by the matter in hand, to which I, out of mischief, would invariably reply: "So?" There must have been other elements in his style that irritated other people, for despite his obvious competence and his outstanding devotion to duty, he didn't quite make it to the top of the administrative tree. Perhaps some of the king-makers were old enough to remember a former Alan and the views he then expressed. No vice-chancellorship or headship of a college came his way, although he let it be known in all the right quarters that he was available. Perhaps he was too available. His retirement was marked by a grand dinner in college at which several speakers praised his contributions to different aspects of university life. The last time I saw him was in a butcher's shop in the city's covered market where he was asking for a pork chop with the dignity of a Roman senator.

And what about Paul? The committee that had given him such a strong recommendation hadn't exaggerated his abilities. Within a year or two he had produced two articles on Homeric language that were judged to be of major importance by the classicists I talked to, and he had begun to prepare a book on the subject. To extend his range, he had decided to take Sanskrit on board – modern European languages he picked up as he went along, almost without effort it seemed to me, as if they were insignificant trifles. What's more, he was proving to be an excellent tutor, perhaps a little severe, but prepared nonetheless to go to a great deal of trouble to remedy the shortcomings of his pupils. None of us had any doubt that Paul was destined for an academic career of the greatest distinction. And then something happened that, to this day, I do not understand.

He had asked whether he might call on me in my laboratory at some convenient time to discuss a private matter. As usual, I suggested morning coffee. To my amazement, the private matter turned out to be that he wanted to read medicine. He gave out that he didn't really want to spend the rest of his days within the narrow confines of classical studies and that he regarded the financial rewards of the academic life as too meagre to be worth the effort. Needless to say, I didn't believe either of these explanations and was convinced that some much more profound event must have occurred to shatter so abruptly the whole basis of what promised to be a highly successful and rewarding life. Characteristically, he had worked out a detailed plan of action. He had gleaned from the university statutes that, given certain exemptions to which he was entitled, he could complete the pre-clinical course in eighteen months or two years, and he proposed then to go to the United States for his clinical training. When I asked him how he intended to finance this, he revealed that he had already unearthed at one of the New York medical schools a lucrative scholarship for which he thought himself especially eligible. I did my best to dissuade him. I pointed out that a great deal of the medical course was insufferably dull, that he was not necessarily cut out for it, and that the financial rewards, even after an interminable period of training, were not predictable. But he was not to be dissuaded.

A couple of years later I marked one of his examination papers. It didn't contain a great deal of information, but the writing was of a quality that one rarely sees in medical students. One of the essays, although it dealt in generalities, was so entertaining that I gave it an alpha mark. Well, he completed his pre-clinical studies on time, won his scholarship in New York as he had predicted, and left. For a year or so, one or other of his friends received the odd letter, from which we gathered that Paul's life was still proceeding according to plan. Then the trickle of correspondence dried up. Someone brought back the news that he had completed his clinical training and was working in one of the large New York medical centres. A little later, I picked up a rumour that he had married. The lady was said to be very rich, but the marriage hadn't lasted long. After that Paul disappeared completely, not only from our lives, but from our thoughts.

Last summer I spent a few hot days in New York to give a lecture

34

and visit some old friends. After the lecture there was a small dinner in one of those extravagantly expensive American establishments that pass for French restaurants. The lecture I had given was named after a man who had been not only a distinguished scientist but also a writer of elegant and imaginative prose. As we talked about him, the conversation drifted to medical education and the changes that would have to be made to it if we wanted to produce more people like that. We had gone on to gossip about the few individuals we could think of who had had a formal education in the humanities as well as the sciences, when one of my hosts turned to me and asked: "You don't by any chance know Paul D., do you? I understand he was a classicist in your university many years ago."

And that's how I came to learn that Paul was now a fashionable New York physician, prominent enough to have his photograph appear from time to time in the social pages of the New York Times. Apparently he had had two brief marriages but was now, as far as my informant knew, unmarried. The following morning I looked him up in the telephone directory. His consulting rooms were located in the elegant upper seventies on the East Side, but there was no entry for his home address. I rang the number and was greeted by a smooth-voiced receptionist to whom I explained that Paul and I had once been colleagues, that my short stay in New York was coming to an end, and that I would be most grateful if Paul could find time to have a brief word with me some time that day. The receptionist sounded very pessimistic, explaining that Dr D was an extremely busy man, but she agreed nonetheless to see what could be done and promised to ring me back. About half an hour later, when I had almost given up hope, she did ring back and told me that Dr D could see me for a few minutes at 5.15 pm that day if I could make it. I made it.

His rooms were in a well preserved old brownstone house in one of those delightful streets that run between Madison and Fifth Avenue up near the Metropolitan Museum. Everything about the building, the uniformed porter at the entrance, the oak panelling, the sleek receptionist, spoke of wealth. Paul greeted me with an outstretched hand. He had grown into a slim middle-aged man and still retained something of his old schoolboy air despite the studied Brooks Brothers elegance of his attire and the streaks of silver in his hair. He offered me a dry martini, which, he assured me, would be made perfectly by his receptionist, but since he was so obviously pressed for time, I declined. At my prompting, he talked, with apparent enthusiasm, about the affluent and exciting life he now lived, but he didn't tell me anything I wanted to know. He did not ask about Maurice or Harvey or Alan, his old companions at bridge, or indeed about anyone from his English past; and when, with some relief, I decided that it was time for me to go, I could not help feeling that if Paul ever gave a thought now to the life he had with us, he would view it as if it were an episode from the literature of the ancient world.

My former college is very kind to me, and from time to time I receive an invitation to join in one or other of its commemorative feasts. I was there last month for such an occasion, and when the many courses finally came to an end and we moved off for coffee in the common room, I was impelled by a gust of nostalgia to poke my nose into that small room where Maurice and his companions used to play bridge. The room was dark, but when I switched on the light, I found that very little had changed. The same disgruntled old men still stared down from the walls and the Victorian card table stood, partly folded and a little dusty, in one corner. Were there no more bridge players?

CHAPTER 3

FULL CIRCLE

Dons often fall in love with their pupils, and vice versa. Sometimes this engenders a marriage. Sometimes it breaks one up. Sometimes both. It's a perfectly banal theme to write about. So many hands, skilful and unskilful, have had a go at it, that you might wonder that there is anything left to say. I didn't especially want to write about David W's love affair, which was long overdue, but, as I turned his frustrated life over in my mind, I found that I couldn't leave the love affair out, for what he eventually became is inexplicable without it.

I first came across him when, as a Ph.D. student, I was advised by my supervisor to go and see him about a technical procedure with which I was having some difficulty. My supervisor warned me that he was very shy and rather prickly, but that, if I handled him gently, he might be very helpful for he knew as much about that particular technology as anyone. He was then a lecturer in one of the departments down the road that form a kind of bridge between chemistry and biology, and I had a little difficulty in finding him, for his laboratory was at the end of a long corridor in what seemed to be a kind of basement. When I knocked on the door, a high pitched, almost falsetto, voice called out 'Enter', but when I entered I couldn't at first see anyone in the room. Then the same voice, apparently from on high, said 'Yes?', and I looked up to find him sitting at a small desk perched on a makeshift gallery that you reached by means of a rather unstable-looking ladder.

He was a small, sharp faced, spidery man, of uncertain age but probably in his mid-forties, with jet black hair parted scrupulously down the middle of his head, and what struck you at once was the impression of extraordinary neatness. There was not a hair out of place and his plain dark blue tie was knotted just as it should be, without a crease and in the dead centre of a plain white collar. He explained to me that he had built the gallery himself in order to make more laboratory space, but I would have put it the other way, that the gadgetry he had accumulated in the laboratory had simply crowded him out. I had never seen anything like it. Every square inch of bench was loaded with apparatus of one kind or another, much of it looking very home-made, and a lot more was held in place on the walls by an array of ingenious brackets. He was obviously one of those people who never threw anything away, and, for a moment, I wondered whether his mind might not also be so stuffed with technical detail that he would make an insuperable mountain out of my little mole-hill. But I was quickly disabused. He came down from his perch and with Edwardian courtesy asked me in what way he could be of help. With all due humility (and I am not normally all that humble) I put my problem to him. He saw the point at once, gave it a moment's thought and then, with great tact, suggested, ever so tentatively, where I might have gone wrong and what might be done to put things right. I was rather sceptical about his diagnosis, but I thanked him profusely and went back to my own laboratory to try out his suggestion. Three days later it was abundantly clear that he was absolutely right.

I thought the least I could do was to go back and thank him, and although it was obvious that he was very pleased, he struggled hard to suppress the smile that kept flickering about his small mouth. It must have been rare for him to receive such simple courtesies, for a few days later the post brought a formal invitation to take lunch at his home. He lived in a Victorian semi-detached in one of the less fashionable streets a couple of miles north of the town centre. The doorbell produced a fragment from the chimes of Big Ben and was answered by David himself, impeccably dressed in a dark grey suit. He led me through a hall full of bric-a-brac into what must have been the Victorian parlour, furnished now in accordance with the canons of pre-war suburban good taste.

If I had not already heard a little about her, his wife would have come as a surprise. She was a big, heavy woman, a good head taller than David, and if he was the epitome of neatness, she was a monument to disorder. Her hair, a metallic yellow, but black at the roots, had the lifeless frizziness that comes from too vigorous a permanent wave, and her tweeds, originally green, were spattered with the residue of a morning's gardening. David's shoes were black oxfords that gleamed with polish, hers were floppy brown brogues still covered with mud. She greeted me expansively and introduced me to the other guests, a taxonomic botanist and his schoolteacher wife, and, to make even numbers, a studious-looking young lady who was writing a thesis on some aspect of Elizabethan madrigals. It was David who had prepared the lunch and who served it; his wife's contribution appeared to be limited to a eulogy of his prowess as a cook. It was indeed a good lunch, but I was glad when it was over, for the conversation had been unremittingly formal and dominated by the resonant contralto of David's wife.

But the lunch had one rewarding consequence for me: it was the starting point of a much closer relationship between David and myself than might have been predicted from the disparity in age, outlook and personal style. I have never had much time for the convention that, on social occasions, you must avoid talking about your own subject. On the contrary, it has been my experience that, provided they are comprehensible, people are often at their best when they are talking about something they are genuinely interested in. In any case, during the course of the lunch, when the conversation moved to gardening and the sometimes surprising behaviour of variegated plants, I managed to get in a few remarks about genes and the possibility that some of them might yet be found to reside in places other than the chromosomes. That wasn't the subject of my research at the time, but it was a question that interested me, and it must have sparked off something in David too, for a week or so later he rang me to ask whether I could find the time to talk to him at greater length about genes and their possible whereabouts. This was, in a way, a surprising development, for David was an orthodox chemist, if ever there was one, and his considerable reputation rested on his talent for devising and increasing the sensitivity of chemical micromethods. I was not aware that, gardening apart, he had any interest in biology. When we had our talk, however, it transpired that it was not actually the biological problem that had captured his imagination, but the possibility that it might be solved by the application of the micromethods of which he was a master. I didn't know enough about these methods to be able to judge whether the gleam in David's eye was a practical possibility, but when I had given him some indication of the amounts of material involved, he didn't seem too discouraged. He came back to me several times over the next few weeks for more detailed information, and then, hesitantly at first, but soon with total commitment, he began to hunt for genes that were not in the chromosomes.

I think I should say that at that time nobody was at all confident that such genes actually existed. There were indeed some curious observations, mostly of a genetical kind, that could be regarded as evidence in favour of the idea, but these observations were also explicable in other ways. The dominant and, it must be admitted, rather arrogant figures who were then laying the foundations of modern molecular biology saw no reason to turn their attention to ill defined phenomena ascribed to hypothetical non-chromosomal genes. They took the view, rightly no doubt, that elucidating the structure and mode of action of classical chromosomal genes gave them more than enough to do. But the attitudes of these gifted men, and more particularly the dogmatic style that many of them adopted in the public exposition of their ideas, generated a climate in which dissenting views were rarely given a fair hearing. I warned David that his new goal might prove to be a will-o'-the-wisp and that, in any case, he was likely to be in for a hard time. He was amazed that anyone could be influenced, even for a moment, by such considerations.

His approach to the problem was very direct. He knew that, except for one brief period when the cell was actually in the process of dividing into two, its chromosomes were sequestered in the cell nucleus. He also knew that genes were made of DNA. So, to begin with, he set himself the task of finding out whether what was left of the cell after you had removed its nucleus contained any DNA. There was evidence based on staining reactions that small amounts of DNA were present in cells in areas outside of the nucleus; but there were doubts about the sensitivity and the specificity of these staining reactions, and David therefore proposed to make the measurements by unequivocal chemical procedures. But to have enough material to do this, he would need to remove the nuclei from large numbers of cells, and he soon found that all the methods that had been described for doing this were inadequate for his purposes. Even the best of them inflicted some damage on the nuclei and hence some leakage of chromosomal components. To find some DNA outside of the nucleus in such circumstances meant nothing.

For a year or more David battled to develop better methods. At first, I provided him with the batches of cells he required, as the facilities for growing them did not appear to be available in his department; but somehow, in his crowded universe, he managed to set up what was needed, and, after that, I simply popped in from time to time to see how he was getting on. His ingenuity was remarkable. Gadgets for doing quite complicated operations grew out of his bench like weeds after summer rain. When, in an obscure technical journal, he finally published his method for removing nuclei from cells, it was incomparably better than anything that had gone before. However, it still wasn't good enough for him. He hadn't yet overcome the problem of contamination by chromosomes released from dividing cells during that brief period when the chromosomes were not sequestered in nuclei. He had indeed found more DNA in the cells after removal of their nuclei than could be accounted for by this source of contamination, but he remained dissatisfied. Then, one day, he began to talk to me about giant cells and wanted to know whether I had ever worked with them.

The giant cells he was interested in were plant cells so huge that it was possible to remove the nucleus from a single cell by simple surgical procedures. The cells that I had supplied him with were animal cells, much too small for this kind of surgical intervention. He had been surprised to learn from what he could glean from the literature that he would need to remove the nuclei from only fifty or so of these giant cells to have more than enough material for his purposes. It so happened that, for another reason, I had a passing interest in one of these giant cells and told him what I knew about it, which wasn't much but which included the essential information that it was very difficult to grow and grew very slowly even under optimal conditions. Of course, this didn't deter David either.

It was at this point that Emma entered his life. He had asked his botanical friend – the one I had had lunch with – whether he knew of any prospective botany graduate who might be interested in joining him in the work on giant cells. It seemed to him that this was a reasonable project for a Ph.D. student, and Emma, who was about to take her final examinations and hadn't yet made up her mind what to do with herself, jumped at the offer. When I first saw her I thought how apt it was that she should be a botanist and be called Emma. At that time you didn't often see a girl who, without modification, would fit perfectly into a Victorian genre painting entitled "Young Lady Botanising". Blue jeans were then all the rage, but Emma always wore plain skirts to well below the knee and blouses, generally white, with long sleeves. She was almost too slim and her hair, bordering on blond, was done up in a single thick plait that crowned a face of completely conventional prettiness.

David and Emma hit it off at once for she appeared to be no less meticulous than he was, although, as far as I could see, she didn't have anything like the technical ingenuity that was his hallmark. It was Emma who got the cells to grow and took on the task of maintaining the cell cultures. These were housed in the botany department, but all the chemical analyses were done in David's laboratory. Many months went by before he had anything to report, and then, when he was ready, he simply let me know as a matter of fact, and not for dispute, that his giant cells contained easily measurable amounts of DNA that were not in the nucleus. When he spelt out just how much DNA there was elsewhere in the cell, I found the figures hard to believe and cast about for other explanations of the results he had obtained. One explanation that occurred to me was that the huge plant cells might be harbouring bacteria and that it was the bacterial DNA that was being measured. Contamination of cell cultures by bacteria and other micro-organisms was never very far from my mind, but the possibility had never occurred to David, which did not surprise me, or to Emma, which surprised me a great deal, for, as a botanist, she must have been taught a lot about the intimate associations that exist between plants and bacteria.

They sent a few of the cell cultures to the bacteriologists who promptly reported that they were indeed teeming with micro-organisms of one kind or another. So they began all over again, seeking this time to get the cultures established under sterile conditions. This had never been done before, and more than a year went by before David was able to announce that even when the cells were free from contaminating microorganisms, they still contained an unexpectedly large amount of DNA that was not in the cell nucleus. David decided that the time had come to make a public presentation of the work.

There was an international conference due to take place in London a few months later, and he wrote to the chairman of the organising committee to enquire whether what he had to say might find a place in the programme. A rather pompous reply informed him that, in principle, all the lectures had already been allocated, but that if there were any unexpected cancellations, the chairman would bear him in mind. This chairman, whose scientific contributions were difficult to discern, had made a notable career for himself by organising conferences and writing obtuse reviews. It didn't at all surprise me that he failed to see the importance of what David was doing. However, while he was making other arrangements, David received a second letter, this time from a less well known, but perhaps more percipient, member of the organising committee, offering to fit him in at the end of one of the symposia that were scheduled for the final day of the conference. David accepted.

International conferences were not then as disgusting as they are today, but they were unpleasant enough. The parade of intellectual arrogance, the ruthlessness, the self-advertisement were already apparent, and many participants had begun to limit their presentations to material that had either been published before in some other form or that was about to be published. Nobody seemed willing to give anything away. I turned up on the last day just to hear David. The symposium in which he was the last speaker was not well attended. The big names had already gone home, and most of the seats in the lecture theatre were empty. He was preceded by three slick young men who confidently expounded a view of the cell so simple that it made one wonder that there was anything left to investigate.

A handful of listeners trickled out just before David began. He was a poor lecturer, constantly referring to his notes and delivering his information without gesture or modulation of his precise, rather pedantic, speech. He spent most of his time elaborating on the

43

methodological difficulties that had had to be overcome. He dealt with his work on animal cells rather summarily, burying his technical virtuosity in the conclusion that the work had in the end not proved decisive. Then he turned to the giant plant cells but, once again, concentrated on technicalities. I think it likely that most of his audience had slumbered off before he got round to making his main point, but finally he did tell them that his giant cells contained large amounts of DNA that was not in the chromosomes of the cell nucleus. In the few minutes allowed for discussion there was only one comment. It came from one of the young speakers who had preceded him. "Well", he said "you do seem to have a lot of DNA there, but it might not be doing anything. It might just be junk." David made no answer.

The next time I spoke to David I was amazed to find that he had taken that comment seriously. He felt that it was incumbent on him to show not only that the DNA was there, but that it did something. Now in those days we had only the vaguest idea of how genes transmitted their messages to other parts of the cell, but we did know that those messages were contained in a substance called RNA which was made on the DNA of the genes and then released. So David set himself the task of finding out whether his giant cells could still make RNA after their nuclei had been removed. Once again, he disdained to use the rather crude and indirect techniques that were then available and developed a new chemical micromethod that permitted minute amounts of RNA to be measured with great accuracy. It was a much more difficult problem to determine whether the cells made RNA after the removal of their nuclei than it was to show that they still contained DNA, and many months went by before David was satisfied with his results. But eventually he was able to say, with complete confidence, not only that his cells contained a lot of DNA that was not in the chromosomes, but also that they continued to make RNA after their nuclei had been removed.

The paper in which David and Emma wrote up their findings I regard as a classic – modest, concise and definitive. But it is, I fear, a forgotten classic. David didn't want to put it into one of the fashionable biological journals that might have made a fuss of it, and perhaps even given it a puff in one of the daily papers. His reason for this was that he didn't want his exposition of the work to be constrained to a limited number of pages, and he certainly didn't want to have his prose tinkered with by opinionated editors, which was the usual practice in such journals, especially the weeklies. My view is that the fashionable journals wouldn't have taken the paper anyway. It appeared in a conservative biochemical journal that was perfectly respectable, but not much read by the new wave of molecular biologists who were then making all the running. I doubt that they would have taken much notice of it even if they had read it, but the total silence that greeted its appearance remains a source of astonishment. David was at first perplexed by the absence of any response to his work. He knew that he had provided a definitive answer to a biological question of the greatest importance, and he expected that this would be acknowledged. At one point he asked me, in all seriousness, whether molecular biologists were always so reticent. It was, of course, completely against his nature to do anything about the lack of recognition; for him, self-advertisement was beneath contempt. So he simply accepted, with much greater equanimity than I could have mustered in the circumstances, that he might have to wait a long time before the significance of his contribution was properly appreciated. Emma's Ph.D. thesis, which contains all the experimental detail, is also a classic, but I give David most of the credit for that.

What he took to be the reticence of the molecular biologists did, however, prove to be decisive for David in one respect. He began to distance himself again from biological problems, and it was not long before he closed down the work on giant cells altogether. I am not sure that at that stage in the development of our knowledge, there was much more that chemical ingenuity could do to clarify the structure or the function of the genes that he had identified, but it seemed to me that his withdrawal from biology might have been determined less by his assessment of what was technically possible at the time than by his disillusionment. He found a source of funds that permitted him to employ Emma as a research assistant, and together they turned their attention to the further development of chemical micromethods.

It was in the last stages of the work on giant cells that I noticed the change in David's appearance. It was at first simply the absence of a tie that caught my attention. David adhered to the practice of an earlier generation in always wearing a tie to work, and its absence, which would have been unremarkable in most people, especially in the summer months, was, in his case, striking. A little later, floral shirts began to make their appearance and, on cooler days, a turtle-neck sweater. The next thing that happened was that his conservative dark trousers were edged out by blue jeans, and finally, the central parting disappeared from his hair which was now cropped short and brushed vigorously back. It was all too obvious that David was chasing his youth. I didn't notice much change in Emma except on one rather awkward occasion when I bumped into them both as they were walking out of a cinema which in those days specialised in foreign films. There was no reason why David and Emma shouldn't go and see 'La Ronde' if they wanted to, but they seemed rather embarrassed at meeting me on that occasion, and the few words we exchanged were curiously stilted. That was the first time I saw Emma with lipstick on.

I can't say that I was too surprised when I heard that David had left his wife and moved with Emma into a small terrace house close by the railway station. The divorce was protracted and acrimonious, and it left David a poorer man but not, I think, either sadder or wiser. David and Emma had been living together for two or three years before they were finally able to marry. I don't know exactly where or when the marriage took place, for I saw less and less of David after he stopped working on biological problems. This was not only because our scientific interests had drifted apart. The truth was that I didn't really much like Emma, and I think she sensed this. Nonetheless, once every couple of years or so David did ask me to lunch in the little terrace house, and I always accepted. The last time I went I was struck by the change that had taken place in Emma. She had put on a great deal of weight and now conveyed an unmistak-able impression of matronly authority. It was David who prepared the lunch and who served it; Emma extolled the virtuosity of his cooking.

About ten years after David's classic paper had appeared, molecular biologists began to be interested in chloroplasts. These are the microscopic structures that carry the chlorophyll in plant cells; they harness the energy of sunlight to synthesise substances that the cell can use for growth. They are not to be found in the cell nucleus. It very quickly became apparent that each chloroplast had its own set of genes and that these genes produced messages in the form of RNA. Indeed, many people came to believe that chloroplasts were the descendants of primitive microorganisms that had invaded the cell at an early stage of its evolutionary history and then taken up permanent residence there. Not one of the torrent of papers released by this new vision of chloroplasts made any mention of David's paper or of the controversy that had once surrounded the idea that the cell might contain genes that were not in the chromosomes of the cell nucleus. David's conclusive experiments had sunk without trace.

I had no reason to visit David in his laboratory once he had closed down the work on giant cells, but when the first of the chloroplast papers appeared, I felt that I had to go and tell him about it, as I was sure he wouldn't any longer be reading the kind of journal in which the paper had appeared. His laboratory had reverted to the state in which I first saw it, and he was perched, as before, in his gallery. I had heard from some of the other chemists whom I met from time to time that his experiments were no longer interesting. He still worked assiduously at refining chemical micromethods, but nobody could see precisely what purpose this meticulous work now served. The general opinion was that his recent papers were arid. When he came down from his perch I asked after Emma and was told that she was well. He volunteered no further information, however, and I couldn't help feeling that he didn't particularly want to talk about her. He listened to what I had to say about chloroplasts, but in a completely detached way. It was clear that he didn't now care in the least where genes might be located in the cell or what they might be doing. He seemed to be entirely without rancour or regret that his own work had been overlooked. Recognition, to say nothing of fame, was now a matter of complete indifference to him. I felt I had to change the subject and, rather at a loss, asked him whether he still enjoyed living so close to the centre of the town. He said he did but greatly missed the larger garden he used to have.

I would have predicted that David was going to live to a ripe old age. The years had treated him gently. He was as wiry and nimble as ever, and his hair had only the faintest touch of grey. But the Fates are blind and they take no notice of statistics. He collapsed one evening while digging a vegetable plot in his minute back garden and was dead before they got him to hospital. Every now and again I pass Emma in the street, but she never seems to recognise me.

CHAPTER 4

A MEMORIAL SERVICE

As the years go by and the circle of my friends diminishes I have reluctantly become a connoisseur of memorial services. In this ancient place, instinctively conservative and much given to ceremony, these occasions rarely deviate from the ritual patterns imposed by tradition: the sentences, an ordered sequence of lessons, hymns and prayers, the address, another hymn, another prayer and, finally, the benediction. It is not a rubric that encourages innovation. But once in a way, an imaginative next of kin introduces a variation that breaks the mould.

Erich Z's memorial service took place on a brilliantly sunny morning, so I can't use the weather to help me set the mood, as writers often do. In fact, the sombre greys and blacks gathering in the small church that formed the centre of the village in which he spent his last years seemed peculiarly out of place against the floral exuberance of that perfect May day. There were not many of us, and it was all too easy to tick off the last handful of that extraordinary cohort of scholars who, like Erich, had been driven to our shores in the 1930s by the storms of continental Europe. It will not be long before they will all have passed into history, but what an immense difference they made. There is hardly a discipline in this university that has not been transformed by their presence, the cobwebs of dilettantism blown away by the cold wind of a deeper dedication. When, an age ago, I thumbed through my first copy of the University Calendar, I was amazed that any university could have interests so catholic as to include a Readership in Byzantine Music; when, later, I learned that the post had been especially created to accommodate a displaced Austrian composer, the surprise turned to admiration.

There was no organ music – no familiar melody to conjure up remembrance of other such days. Instead, behind the altar sat a quartet, an amateur group I should have thought, young enough to be undergraduates; and when we were assembled they began the adagio from Mozart's F major Oboe Quartet. They played beautifully and the oboist was certainly no amateur. We were told later that Erich, who was intimately familiar with every note of Mozart's music, was particularly attached to that quartet. When the adagio came to an end, an unadorned version of the traditional Anglican service began, but when it came to the address we were given something unexpectedly different. Felix B, whose speech still carried the trace of his Berlin origins and whom many regarded as the foremost classical scholar of his day, spoke for three-quarters of an hour about Erich's astonishing gifts, his distinguished family and his unimpeachable academic integrity. But it was not an address as we had come to know it. It was a *laudatio* at home in another tradition; and when the service ended with its customary benediction, the musicians gave us the optimistic rondo from that same Mozart quartet. If you have ever attended an Akademische Gedenkfeier in a German university, you will recognize the lineaments: the deeply serious exposition of the man's life and work, the much-loved chamber music that begins sadly but ends in hope. Only the Rhine wine was missing, and that came later, at Erich's home.

I am not sure that the amalgam of Anglican ritual and German secularism was an unqualified success but, whatever its aesthetic shortcomings might have been, it certainly did reflect the two essential strands in Erich's life. He was born in Würzburg, where his father's family could trace continuous residence back to the Middle Ages, and it didn't take much prompting to induce him to reminisce, perhaps a little sentimentally, about the beautiful old university town in which he had spent his early childhood. But while he was still at primary school, his father, a highly successful physician and a Privatdozent at the university, accepted an invitation to a medical chair in Berlin, and it was the life of that dramatic city that formed the backdrop to Erich's formative years.

Erich's father must have been a remarkable man (and the committee that recommended his appointment to the Berlin chair must have been a remarkable committee) for prejudice against Jews was quite general in German academic life, and especially in academic medicine, long before it was systematised in Hitler's catastrophic legislation. With its deep roots in the history of the country, Erich's family was completely at home in the mainstream of middle class German life and wore their Judaism very lightly, but they had not converted to Christianity, and this was then a serious obstacle to academic advancement. From Erich's accounts of their life in Berlin, it was clear that his father was as successful there as he had been in Würzburg. They lived in a large villa close by the Grunewald where, in the summer, the family would often walk together. It must have been an unusually cultivated household for once, when we were talking together in his living room and Richard Strauss somehow came into the conversation, Erich remarked that he remembered Richard Strauss at the piano in their Berlin home giving them a foretaste of *Intermezzo*, which opened a few weeks later in Dresden. On another occasion, when I happened to mention that the Royal Society had a very interesting portrait of the young Albert Einstein by Max Liebermann, Erich told me that Max Liebermann had done an excellent portrait of his father but this, together with all their other possessions, had disappeared in the Nazi maelstrom.

You might be curious to know how it came about that Erich's path and mine crossed. The introduction was effected by my five-year-old daughter. I had recently moved my young family into our first house, purchased with the largest mortgage that the system allowed, and the children had soon taken to playing on the footpath in front of it. Erich, his great shock of hair already then completely white, and his eyes obscured by pebble lenses, would often shamble by on his way to the shopping centre, and long before I first spoke to him, he and my daughter were already old cronies. I knew where he lived – in a grey, rather neglected house just around the corner – for I passed by that house on my way to the postbox, and in the evenings before the curtains were drawn, I could usually see him through the bay window poring over his books. If I happened to be in the front garden when he went by, we would exchange a few words. Eventually I plucked up my courage and asked him and his wife Betty over for coffee, and that's how our rather incongruous but durable friendship began.

It appears that his extraordinary linguistic gifts became apparent at a very early age. By the time he entered the Französisches Gymnasium, that distinguished school in which much of the instruction was given in French, he had already acquired a good working knowledge of Latin and Greek, largely self-taught, and his teachers recognized from the very beginning that they would have to give him free rein. When he enrolled in the Friedrich Wilhelm University in Berlin to study classical philology, he found he had read most of the authors listed in the curriculum and, as far as I could judge from conversations with him many years later, he must have committed large tracts of their work to memory. He told me that he had attended some lectures given by Wilamowitz but had not found the ponderous generalisations of his last years particularly interesting.

It was in his university days that Erich first became seriously interested in oriental influences on the language and literature of the Greeks and began to assimilate the scripts of the ancient Near East. Nobody seemed to know exactly how many of these he eventually mastered, for the short, but decisive, notes that he communicated to learned journals covered an immense range, and I heard it said by one of his philological colleagues that no subject that ever came up in discussion was so obscure that Erich couldn't have offered a deeply professional contribution to it if he had wanted to. Felix B, who was also studying classical philology in Berlin at the time, told me that in the university it was generally recognised that Erich was a prodigy and completely *hors concours*. He had made a spectacular international debut while still a student by demonstrating that a much debated Hellenistic document had been totally misinterpreted and was actually a free translation of a little known inscription written originally in Middle Persian. Although Felix's studies on the Greek and Latin poets were universally admired as monuments of classical scholarship, he never for a moment regarded himself as being in the same class as Erich, and Felix was not given to false modesty. But Felix stayed with Latin and Greek and was eventually elected into a professorship, whereas Erich remained forever on the sidelines. His main interests were not part of the undergraduate course, and there was hardly anyone about who could make much of ancient Near Eastern languages. His formidable reputation and his immense range finally induced the university authorities, under pressure from both the philologists and the classicists, to create a modest post for him; and in this he remained until he retired.

I found it difficult to believe that this gentle, otherworldly scholar could once have been swept off his feet by a grand passion. This, too, I had from Felix. Erich was then an Assistent on the first rung of what would undoubtedly have been a glittering academic career in Berlin, when, to everyone's surprise, he looked up from his books one day and found himself in love. The young lady had caught his eye in the university library where she sat scrutinising some reproductions of early Greek vases. According to Felix, Erich had broken the ice by asking whether she understood the significance of some obscure symbols painted on one of them, and when it transpired that she did not, he gave her a short tutorial, which was interrupted by one of the librarians ordering them to keep quiet. Erich, in a reckless departure from his normal practice, suggested that they might continue their conversation over a cup of coffee, and they left the library together.

She was a student of art history, the daughter of a well known judge in the Prussian Administrative High Court. Felix described her as an archetypal young Teuton – tall, slim, blond and athletic. But, improbable as their wildly different temperaments may have made it seem, the romance flourished, and it soon began to look as if a marriage was in the offing. Hitler's assumption of power put an end to all that. The young lady's father turned out to be a far from heroic figure, and Felix once showed me an old newspaper cutting with him in the front row of an assemblage of judges, their arms outstretched in a Heil Hitler salute and their judicial robes embellished with a Nazi emblem. She eventually married a young army officer, the bearer of a noble name which, curiously enough, was very familiar to us in this university because several members of that ancient family had over the years been educated here. Felix claimed that Erich never quite got over the betrayal.

Erich was working on manuscripts in the British Museum when, for Jews, the barriers came down on the borders of the Third Reich. By a circuitous route, he received a letter from his father warning him not under any circumstances to return to Germany. Like many others in their position, Erich's parents were convinced that Hitler was a transient aberration and made no move to leave Germany until it was too late. Erich later heard, via a fragile grapevine, that they had been taken to Theresienstadt, but he did not then know that Theresienstadt was merely a way-station on the road to Auschwitz. He never heard from them again.

Erich's spectacular resolution of the controversy surrounding that enigmatic Hellenistic document was well known to our classicists, so that it was not all that difficult for the Academic Assistance Council, which had been established to help refugee scholars, to find a temporary place for him here. Erich once described this as the loneliest period of his life. He had no family in this country and no idea what was happening to the family he had left behind. He lived in a boarding house run by a landlady who viewed him with ill-concealed suspicion, and he did not find it at all easy to adapt to our academic practices. He seems to have been very largely excluded from tutorial teaching, for which I should have thought he had a natural talent, and was asked to give lectures, which he found difficult and pitched at much too high a level to attract a respectable audience. It seems that he had little access then to college common rooms.

At the outbreak of the war, one of the tribunals set up by the Home Office to investigate Germans and Austrians then resident in Britain came to the brilliant conclusion that Erich was an Enemy Alien Category B, which meant that although he was not at once interned, his movements were restricted and he had to report regularly to the police. After Dunkirk, when the Home Office, fearing that the defences of the country might be undermined by a 'fifth column', decided to intern all enemy aliens in category B, Erich found himself in the 'Central Promenade Camp' at Douglas on the Isle of Man. At one point he was under threat of deportation to Canada. During the long months of internment he took an active part in the home-made 'university' that the internees set up there out of their own intellectual resources, and he once told me that at the time he felt more at home in that university than in ours.

When he was released, he made many attempts to find some post in which his talents might be used to further the war effort, but with no success until, on the recommendation of a senior academic who had been seconded to the BBC, he was offered a temporary niche in its foreign language monitoring service. For a time he felt a little less isolated, partly because of the daily contact with his colleagues at work, and partly because in London he was able now and again to meet other fugitives from Germany with whom he could reminisce about the past and despair of the future. As information about the fate of the Jews began to trickle out of Occupied Europe, his gloom deepened, and when VE Day came, what he felt was grim satisfaction, not joy. He was one of the first to go when the BBC began to shed its monitoring staff, and he came back with no great enthusiasm to the temporary academic post that had been secured for him before the war. He moved into another boarding house, this time with a sympathetic landlady, and once more took up the threads of his scholarly work. And then came Betty.

Betty's account of how they began going out together differed in some respects from Erich's, but as far as I could see the initial motivation was simply that the cinema was much more fun in company than alone. There was none of the romantic aura that had surrounded Erich's first great love in Berlin. Indeed, I can't believe that Betty was ever the kind of girl to sustain a romantic aura. She had come down from London to take up a teacher's post in a primary school and was, for the time being, living in the same boarding house as Erich. So they could hardly have avoided each other. But she was exactly what he needed: immensely practical, kind but unsentimental, not in the least overawed by intellectual brilliance, and quintessentially English. I don't think Erich could have come to terms with living in this country if Betty hadn't shown him how to do it. Betty's parents apparently had deep misgivings about her decision to marry him, and although they did their best to make him feel welcome, they never could make head or tail of what he was about. They were greatly disappointed when Betty finally agreed to a registry wedding. Erich had no religious beliefs at all and, as far as I could judge, no religious feelings, but it wasn't his disbelief that made it impossible for him to acquiesce in an Anglican marriage ceremony – and Betty's Anglicanism was as broad as you could find – it was the memory of his slaughtered Jewish parents.

It was several years before they could afford to buy the

nondescript grey house with which they will always be associated in my mind. Indeed, it was not until Erich, at Betty's insistence, agreed to claim the compensation offered by the post-war government of West Germany, that they had enough money to make the purchase. Erich would never call it ' compensation'. "You see, Henry" he explained with a grim smile, "it is not compensation. It is" (and he spelt out the German word syllable by syllable) "Wie-der-gut-mach-ung. It is making things good again!" His attitude to Germany was totally intransigent and remained so for years. As his international reputation grew, invitations to visit the country became more frequent and more flattering, but he invariably ignored them. The turning point came when he received a black-edged card announcing an academic memorial service for an old friend of his father's. It was accompanied by a handwritten note from the man's widow in which she recalled the friendship and added that it would be a great consolation to her if Erich could come. The man had been an eminent physicist and an opponent of the Nazis from the beginning. He had, while it was still possible, publicly defended the reputations of his Jewish colleagues and, when it was no longer possible, he had helped a few of them to escape. It was only his renown that saved him from destruction, and he had spent the war years more or less under house arrest. So Erich went to the memorial service. It must have been a profoundly moving experience, for Betty told me that when he came back, his attitude to Germany had changed. He now argued that if you refused to help the Germans who were labouring to construct a liberal and tolerant society, then, by that very refusal, you helped those who did not want that sort of society. Hesitantly at first, but with greater conviction as time when by, he became involved again in German academic life and, in the end, he accepted honorary degrees from German universities and other distinctions from learned societies there.

Unlike Felix, Erich never really succeeded in winning the affection of his academic colleagues. In fact, they were terrified of him. At first, I found this difficult to understand, for the side of him that I saw was warm, generous, innocent and, at times, even humorous. But it appeared that the indulgence with which he viewed human frailty in other walks of life did not extend to scholarship. His standards there seem to have been impossibly high. I caught a glimmer of this from time to time when, out of simple curiosity, I asked him some question that I assumed he would be able to answer almost without thinking. Sometimes the answer came back in the form of a brief tutorial, reduced to its elements for a beginner, but sometimes his only reply was to say, rather crisply: "I have no idea, Henry. I have not studied the primary sources." I later learned that, in philological circles, this phrase was laughingly referred to as his signature tune, and that he really did refuse to discuss any question whatever unless he was familiar with the primary sources. But he was familiar with a far greater range of primary sources than anybody else. In seminars he sat largely silent, a brooding presence that inhibited discussion. When he did speak, his intervention was decisive, but more often than not destructive. His presence in the audience made lecturers nervous. I was told that with a single book review he demolished the reputation of a classicist who, one way and another, had achieved a position of some consequence in British university circles.

Erich was eventually elected to the Fellowship of the British Academy, but long after Felix. This distinction, which one might have thought would be a matter of indifference to a man of his extraordinary gifts, in fact gave him great pleasure, not, of course, because he needed that stamp of approval for his scholarship, but because he took his election to mean that his professional colleagues at last found him personally acceptable. On the other hand, he was not at all regarded as a forbidding figure in the college where he had modest dining rights. It was not a college given to generous gestures, and he was never offered a fellowship there, for his contribution to undergraduate tutorial teaching, which was then as now the decisive consideration, was much too small to warrant it. I happened to be a dinner guest at that college one evening when he came in. He was warmly received, even fussed over a little, and after coffee he entertained us all with colourful tales of Isherwood's Berlin as it really was. It was as if for him scholarship was a world apart, a kind of sanctuary where much more stringent moral rules applied, where total dedication was mandatory, where levity was out of place and shoddiness unforgivable.

I was very pleased when Betty asked us to join them in a little party she was having to celebrate Erich's sixtieth birthday. Felix was there, of course, and Erwin, who had opened up a whole new area of research in particle physics, and Bernhard whose studies in international law were canonical. From time to time one or other of them recalled some incident from their past, a German past that I did not share, but I felt nonetheless as if I had been made an honorary member of an exclusive club. Felix made the briefest of speeches and we all drank Erich's health. It was at this party that I first met Erich's son, John, and renewed acquaintance with John's daughter, Bettina. John was apparently making a successful career for himself in a London merchant bank, but Betty had once told me, with some bitterness, that that was not his first choice. A distinguished undergraduate career had led him to hope that he might enter the diplomatic service, but when he came to apply he learned to his dismay that he was not eligible. It appears that to be eligible for the diplomatic service, both your parents have to be British born. Bettina I had met some years earlier when Erich, displaying to perfection the art of being a grandfather, used to take her for a walk past our house. She was then a shy, thoughtful little girl with dark curly hair and sad brown eyes, and I imagined I could detect in the way she frowned when she was puzzled a resemblance to Erich. I no longer saw any such resemblance in the precocious young lady who was helping Betty pass round the canapés and who informed me, among other things, that she had recently been introduced to science at her school, found it interesting and intended to make a career of it.

Erich was nearing retirement when his great book finally appeared. He had reached middle age before he felt confident enough to begin and it had taken him almost a decade to write. There had been some difficulty with our own university press, and the immensely complex task of typesetting in more than a dozen ancient languages was eventually undertaken by a West German publishing house. The original owner of this firm had been dispossessed by the Nazis, but the business had been returned to members of his family after the war. Although the work was written in English, it was a lineal descendant of those exhaustive German treatises that used to masquerade under the deceptive title 'Handbuch': three massive volumes that left no stone unturned. It made a front page review in the *Times Literary Supplement*. In those days reviewers were anonymous and their identity a closely guarded secret. But, whoever it was, he was well aware of the magnitude of what had been achieved. He did not limit himself to that stereotyped seal of approval – the conclusion that a book was likely to remain the standard work for some time. He frankly gave it as his view that the work was without significant predecessors and was unlikely ever to be surpassed. I wrote Erich a note of congratulation and received in reply the assurance that the work contained some serious errors that the reviewer had overlooked.

The other thing that happened as Erich approached retirement was that Betty decided that she wanted to end her days in an English village. I was not aware that she had any deep roots in country life, but she had set her heart on a vision she had of rural England, and none of the obvious disadvantages of such a move made much impression on her. It was a curious reversal of roles. It had always been Betty who rehearsed the practical considerations and Erich who indulged in improbable fantasies. Now it was Erich who pointed out that they would be cut off from their friends, that they might not easily integrate into a close-knit village community, that access to libraries and museums would become much more difficult. But Erich was so accustomed to deferring to Betty in matters of this kind that his eventual agreement was a foregone conclusion.

In the summer before he retired they sold their old grey house and moved into a not very picturesque cottage in one of the less spoiled villages about fifteen miles out of town. After that, I did not see Erich often, but when we did manage to get together it was clear that all his forebodings had come to pass. The centres of village life were the church and the pub. Erich, of course, did not go to church, which precluded his having more than formal relations with the church party in the village, and no stretch of the imagination could encompass a picture of Erich happily swapping stories with the *habitués* of the pub. He did, however, mention, with a shrug of the shoulders that suggested puzzlement more than anything else, that Betty had begun to attend church pretty regularly, which, as far as he knew, was something she hadn't done since childhood.

Erich didn't much like driving, and certainly not on the road from that village into town, but there were only four buses a day and they took an hour to make the journey. So his work was severely curtailed and he could not hide his immense frustration. He was not indifferent to the beauties of the countryside, but it did not have for him the rich nostalgic associations that it had for Betty. It was as if the move to that village was just one more dislocation in his profoundly dislocated life. When, some three or so years after they had moved, an intractable cough at last forced him to see a doctor, he was not too dejected to hear that his days were numbered.

The memorial service was Betty's idea. Erich had asked to be cremated but had said nothing about a memorial service, perhaps because the idea that there might be one had never crossed his mind. Betty asked Felix to give the address, and it was he who suggested the modifications to the service that had their origins in the traditions of the Akademische Gedenkfeier. My first reaction to all this was surprise, for I had no doubt that Erich would not have chosen to be commemorated in a church that was not his own and whose services he had never attended; but when I thought a little more about it I concluded that he would not have objected to Betty giving thanks for his life and work in her own fashion.

You must by now be wondering why I felt it necessary to write about Erich. Well, there are two reasons. The first is that I could find no better way of paying him my own last respects; and the second is that there is an epilogue to his life that is so remarkable you will have difficulty in believing it. Bettina turned out to be as good as her word. She completed an impeccable undergraduate career in biochemistry and then asked whether I would accept her as a Ph.D. student. Needless to say, I was delighted at the prospect and she rapidly showed herself to be as competent in the laboratory as she had been as an undergraduate. She had grown into a slim, elegant brunette with just the slightest suggestion of the East in her features, but nothing now that I could trace back directly to Erich. The precocious self-confidence had simmered down to something that I could best describe as poise.

She had been with me for about a year when I received a letter from Tübingen. It came from a young man whose signature revealed that he must be a member of that aristocratic family that had for years been sending its young men to us for their education. It was the name that marriage had conferred on Erich's first great love. The young man had excellent scientific credentials and wanted to work with me in a postdoctoral capacity for a couple of years. He gave me the names of two referees to whom I wrote and both of them recommended him in the most glowing terms. So I agreed to take him, and in due course Otto von H knocked on my door to announce his arrival.

I don't suppose there is such a thing as a classical aristocratic head, but, if there isn't, Otto's certainly fitted our preconceptions. His delicate, almost girlish features were dominated by a high forehead made even more prominent by a hairline that was beginning to recede at the corners. Rimless glasses softened the look in his grey-blue eyes and his fair hair was combed smoothly back. But there was nothing in him of the stiffness or formality that one might have expected to see in his forebears. He was, of course, polite, but completely relaxed, and his English was faultless. I asked him whether he was closely related to the military von H (the man who had finally put paid to Erich's romantic hopes in Berlin). "Yes" he replied "that was my grandfather. He was killed in action on the Eastern Front."

I put Otto in a laboratory at the other end of the corridor where he pretty quickly demonstrated that he knew what he was about. As time went by, I learned a little more about him and the views he held. He was an exemplar of the post-war generation of young Germans who had rejected, sometimes violently, the attitudes of their grandparents and the prevarications of their parents – a passionate democrat, a liberal in the best sense of the word, and a committed European. I can imagine that it was people like Otto that Erich hoped to encourage when he finally persuaded himself to take an interest again in German academic life. But Otto was by no means an indigestible dose of highmindedness. He wrote a riotously funny skit for the departmental Christmas party, and everyone seemed to like him.

One evening, as I came down the stairs, I saw Bettina and Otto leaving the laboratory together. A few days later, I noticed them going off to lunch and, before long, except when they were at work, I hardly ever saw them apart. It is a source of great regret to me that I was not able to accept the invitation to their wedding. It took place a few weeks after Bettina had finished writing up her excellent Ph.D.

thesis and Otto's stay in the department was nearing its end. They were both offered excellent jobs in Tübingen. About a year after they had settled there I received a card announcing the birth of a son. His name was Erich.

CHAPTER 5

FRAUD

Sometimes when I am asked to give a lecture in New York, they put me up at a pretty fancy hotel. The one I stayed at last was fancier than usual. At the reception desk there was an array of smooth young men and pretty girls, all dressed in severe black suits and black bow ties. The bow ties, I suppose, were meant to convey an impression of high class efficiency but, on the girls, they reminded me of Hugh Hefner's bunnies. The one to whom I presented myself sized me up at a glance and naturally decided that I was not one of the world's big spenders. I got a smile, but it was not one of her best. But the bellboy who took my luggage up to the room that had been assigned to me was all smiles, and, after he had turned on the lights and showed me how the television worked, he remained smiling at the door until I had found a couple of dollars for him.

When, jet-lagged, I went down to dinner, I was shown to my table by a dazzling redhead in an iridescent green miniskirt, who teetered across the room in unmanageably high heels. Now I've nothing against dazzling redheads in miniskirts, but in my experience desire militates against the desire to eat, and that particular redhead was not, in any case, the aperitif I needed. The menu was a splurge of hyperboles spiked with misused Gallicisms. Each dish was not only described in colourful detail, it was extolled. There was nothing that wasn't delicious, luscious, mouth watering, succulent and so on, until the epithets ran out. Long experience enabled me to decode this immortal prose and reach the bleak conclusion that the chef was no genius. When the waiter, immensely superior, finally turned up, he treated me to a recitation of the day's special dishes, once again a torrent of superlatives. I settled for lamb chops and American apple pie. It took the best part of two hours to get the meal served and eaten, and when I had finished the evening was gone. I went back up to my room and read my paperback for a while before turning in. There was, as you might expect, nothing watchable on television apart from the soft porn which you can conjure up on a special set of buttons that add a few dollars to your hotel bill. I was in no mood for that.

I had arranged to have lunch the following day with an old friend, Robert S. I found him in the lobby and we agreed that we could do without the hotel dining room. Instead, we went to a nearby eating house run without affectation by a cheerful Greek family. I'd been there often before and liked the place because the people who ate there weren't all desperately trying to be somebody else – office workers, salesmen, shop girls, an occasional van driver, many of them obviously regulars who enjoyed swapping a joke or a bit of gossip with the proprietors. New York without the hype. Robert had aged a great deal since last we met, and as he slumped down at the table I no longer saw the distinguished and masterful scientist that I was familiar with, but a tired old man. I knew what had wreaked the havoc and would not, of course, have mentioned it, but Robert insisted on bringing the matter up.

"What can you do, Henry, if the most gifted graduate student you've ever had decides to cheat his way to fame, if he's an expert at fabricating experimental evidence, if each day's work is a masterpiece of meticulous deception?"

It had been a cause *célèbre*. The spectacular discovery had been announced at a news conference and had spun around the world on the front pages of newspapers. I remember how Robert had basked in the publicity, delighted not only at the importance of what had been done, but also because the work appeared to vindicate one of his pet theories. In the ensuing weeks he gave many lectures on the subject at scientific centres all over the United States and Europe, and his glittering exposition altogether eclipsed the graduate student who had generated the data. But it was not long before doubt began to cast its threatening shadow. First, one of the most professional of the West Coast laboratories announced that it was not able to confirm some aspects of the work. A little later, a team in Boston with an unrivalled reputation in that particular field reported something else that was not repeatable. Robert struggled hard, and for far too long, to salvage some remnants from the wreck, but in vain. In the end he had to publish a complete, and contrite, retraction. He never got over it.

As I watched him recounting his tale, no doubt for the umpteenth time, I felt infinitely sorry for him, for his sins in the matter had been all too human and his many scientific contributions had until then been impeccable. All the same, I couldn't help recalling an exchange I had had with my own uncompromising supervisor while I was still a graduate student. I had asked him, in accordance with what was then the proper convention, whether he would do me the honour of adding his name to one of my early papers. "No." he replied coldly. "I don't put my name on papers unless I have made a material and personal contribution to the work". Would he have regarded Robert's guidance by remote control as a material and personal contribution?

The cold wind that blew Robert off his pedestal once came pretty close to me. At the time, I had a rather complacent attitude to fraud in science. It seemed to me that scientific cheats were gamblers who had lost touch with reality. If they fabricated data on a minor question of no great interest to anyone, they might well escape detection, but then there was no reward. If, however, they cheated in an area of research that commanded widespread attention, then it was only a matter of time, and usually not a very long time, before they were caught out. Unless, by a miracle, the falsification turned out to be a true reflection of reality. But the chances of that happening were not much better than the likelihood of drawing three cards to a straight flush. And the penalty for fraud, once detected, was drastic: the irrevocable destruction of a scientific career. So I regarded cheating in science as a mild form of madness – going for broke against all the odds. Francis changed my mind.

I was rather hesitant about taking him on. His examination results had been excellent, but there were hints in the reports of his tutors that his undergraduate career had not been without problems. That didn't bother me for, in my experience, if they weren't temperamental they weren't any good. But when he came in for interview I began to have doubts. To begin with, there was the way he was dressed. Now I am completely inured to eccentricity of dress in my prospective Ph.D. students. Most of them come for interview in whatever they happen to be wearing that day and make no special effort to spruce themselves up. It is not studied informality, but an unfeigned indifference to outward appearance which, in some respects, I find admirable. Of course, there is the occasional self-conscious aesthetic outrage and, very infrequently, some girl who, for the hell of it, gets dressed to kill. All that is par for the course.

But Francis was different. He looked like a Victorian bank clerk who had been dismissed from his post for some misdemeanour and was desperately seeking another. He wore a grey serge suit which I would guess he had since schooldays, for the trousers, freshly pressed for the occasion, stopped short a good three inches above the ankle. His shirt was surmounted by an ill-fitting detachable collar out of which there protruded a long thin neck and a narrow head with black hair plastered down over it much as in Aubrey Beardsley's self portrait. The curriculum vitae he had sent me revealed that he had been the star pupil at a small school in Sheffield, but there was not much evidence that he had done anything other than apply himself to his books. A hard-earned scholarship had brought him to us. I assumed that he must have come from a genuine working class background, and the motivation to succeed was very strong. But his manner was a bit too deferential, and he ended every second sentence with an almost military 'Sir'. He was as taut as an overwound mainspring and at the slightest increase in tension I felt sure he would snap.

Experimental science can be a very depressing occupation. Most of the time, things don't work. Whether you succeed in the end will be determined as much by your character as by your intelligence. My worry about Francis was whether he was robust enough to withstand repeated failure. I asked him why he wanted to do research and received the answer I like least. He wanted to do something with his life, he assured me, that would be of benefit to mankind. I like it better when they tell me that they don't yet know what they want to do with their lives, that experimental work looks a more interesting way of passing the time of day than lots of other jobs they've considered, and that they'd welcome the chance to have a go at it. I told Francis that I would write to him in a few days' time, after I'd interviewed the other applicants, but I had more or less made up my mind that he wouldn't do. I am not sure what made me hesitate when I came to write him that letter. Perhaps it was the feeling that I might be doing him an injustice and that life would probably dish him out enough of that without any help from me; perhaps it was the fact that his background and mine had much in common.

I made a serious mistake when I decided what laboratory he should work in, for I put him with Christopher. Christopher, who had already been with me for a year, was everything that Francis wasn't – elegant, composed, expensively educated and naturally at ease with everyone about him. And despite a personal style that could, without exaggeration, be described as debonair, he was deeply committed to his work and very good at it. It was not that it hadn't occurred to me that Christopher and Francis might not be miscible, but much of the equipment that they would both need to use was already in the laboratory that Christopher occupied and it seemed sensible to put Francis there too.

I do not ask my Ph.D. students to waste their time on scholastic problems, problems where the outcome is, in principle, known, and diligent measurements will produce a competent thesis within the prescribed number of years. The problems I set them are genuinely important questions at the forefront of enquiry, and I explain to them at the outset that this is a policy that involves an element of risk. For I cannot guarantee that their efforts will be crowned with success, however hard they apply themselves. If they are imaginative (and lucky) they will make a contribution to the field that will ensure them a place in the sun; but there is no foretelling what difficulties might arise or whether they can be overcome. What I can guarantee is that by the time they finish they will have learned what real research is about, will have acquired a wide range of technical experience and will, at the very least, have accumulated the modest amount of material required for a Ph.D. I have never had a graduate student who hesitated to take the risk.

I was also wrong in my assessment of the technical complexity of the problem I suggested for Francis. Since I didn't think that he had the resilience to bounce back after failure, I set him a task that I expected would be more straightforward than some of the experiments we attempt. And so it proved, to begin with. He got to work very quickly and within a few weeks had devised an ingenious new technique for making the measurements that we were sure would be needed. I was at first rather impressed by the meticulous care that he lavished on even the simplest of operations. At the end of each day, he would spend ten minutes or more tidying up his bench, and his laboratory notes, written in a minute, almost calligraphic, hand were a model of precision. It was only when I noticed that the coloured pencils on his desk were always in the same place and arranged in the same order that I began to wonder whether the line between meticulous care and obsession might not have been crossed. Still, the work continued to go well and, as his self-confidence grew, I thought I noticed some relaxation in his manner. Once, as I entered their laboratory, I actually found Francis and Christopher laughing together about something or other. There did not at that time seem to be any tension between them, but I could not avoid the impression that Francis was pitting himself against Christopher and was determined to surpass him.

It's a very lucky Ph.D. student who doesn't strike at least one bad patch. For Francis, the trouble began when the assay he had devised failed to behave predictably in a new set of experimental conditions. There was nothing too unusual about that, and he at once began to probe the difficulty in his characteristically methodical way. I was confident that he would not be held up for long. But as the months went by and he made no further progress, I began to wonder whether the new technique might not be seriously defective, even if it had yielded consistent results in the early stages of the investigation. I kept my doubts to myself, however, for he was becoming rather gloomy and I didn't want to send him back to square one prematurely. I felt sure that he would find his own way there if it became necessary. I did, however, notice that his relations with Christopher had deteriorated. I put this down to scientific rivalry, but it soon became apparent that whatever scientific rivalry there might have been, it was compounded by a deeper rivalry of quite another, and more primitive, kind.

There was a new technician in the department, a very pretty girl called Jenny, who, naturally enough, was the centre of a good deal of young male attention. I gathered via the grapevine that Francis was besotted with her and was pursuing her with predictably serious intentions. She, of course, much preferred Christopher whose intentions were less serious but more appealing. So Francis was casually dismissed. That did it. For three weeks he disappeared, and when he came back he was almost unrecognisable. He had grown the beginnings of a straggly beard, his hair was matted and he smelt as if he had not had a bath since he cleared out. My guess was that he had sought some kind of a solution in drugs, and I determined to keep a close eye on him. However, much to my relief, he quickly settled down, removed the beard and got to work. It was not long before I noticed that the pencils on his desk were again aligned in their proper order.

A couple of months later, Francis came to me with a set of figures that were quite remarkable. It was obvious at a glance that he had not only ironed out the difficulties with his new assay, but had also greatly increased its sensitivity. Indeed, I'd never seen better results with that kind of measurement. He needed praise, and I gave it to him, but I also questioned him at some length about what the problem had been and how he had overcome it. I did this out of genuine curiosity and not at all because I was suspicious, although I remember being rather surprised that the impediment had been such a minor one and that it had taken him so long to overcome it. I meant to go along and actually see the assay in operation, but somehow didn't get round to it.

Francis now began to produce results of the greatest interest. At that time an army of biochemists around the world were looking at enzymes in cancer cells and in the normal cells from which they were derived, in the hope that they might find some enzymatic activity that was peculiar to the cancer cells. Volumes had been written cataloguing such studies, but no one had discovered any activity that distinguished cancer cells categorically from their normal counterparts. The technique that Francis had devised measured the individual activities of two linked enzymes for which no good assay had previously been available. Without revealing his plan to me, he began to measure these activities in a range of different cancer cells and in whatever normal cells he could get hold of. That was not at all the direction in which I had intended the research to go. Indeed, had he discussed it with me, I would have discouraged him from going off on that tack. For one thing, I dislike that kind of mindless survey; and for another, I did not believe that any enzyme would be found that was genuinely specific for cancer cells. I had what I thought were good reasons for this view and was therefore amazed, even if a little disgruntled at not having been consulted about the change of direction, at the next set of results that Francis brought me to see. What he had found in all of the thirty or so cancers that he had looked at was that one of the two linked enzymes was absent, whereas both enzymes were present in the more limited range of normal tissues that he had managed to collect.

Now that was a different proposition altogether. For while I would have been very sceptical if he had found an enzyme that was peculiar to cancer cells, I was all too ready to believe that an enzyme that was present in normal cells might be absent or defective in cells that had become cancerous. Indeed, I had long advocated the theory that the formation of a cancer cell involved the loss of normal cell functions and not the acquisition of new functions. Francis's missing enzyme was thus exactly what I was looking for. So I stifled my reservations about the kind of approach that he had decided to adopt and urged him instead to extend his measurements to certain less common forms of cancer and, above all, to strengthen his data on normal tissues. I felt a little guilty about jumping on Francis's bandwagon, but, whatever views I might have held about good experimental method, I accepted that no scientist could afford to look down his nose at luck. Francis's second report summarised the data on more than fifty cancers and some twenty different kinds of normal tissue. The results were dramatically clear: all the normal tissues had both the enzymes and all the cancers only one. Although we did not as yet have any idea of the significance of this observation in terms of the overall organisation of the cell, it was a finding of such obvious importance that I suggested to Francis that he prepare a draft of his work for publication.

It is the normal practice for a graduate student to publish his first paper with his supervisor as a co-author. This is reasonable, for the subject chosen for investigation is usually some extension of the supervisor's own research, and the work is, at least initially, closely monitored by him. Nonetheless, although I went through Francis's inelegant draft with a fine-tooth comb, I felt very uneasy about putting my name to the paper. This was not because I had any doubts about it, but, as I worked over the text, the words of my supervisor, long since dead, kept running through my head: "I don't put my name on papers unless I have made a material and personal contribution to the work". I had indeed suggested to Francis that those two enzymes were worth investigating, but he alone had developed the assay and, had I known about it, I would have opposed the decision to compare cancer cells with the normal cells from which they were assumed to have been derived. So, in the end, despite the temptation to have my name associated with a discovery of such importance, I told Francis that I didn't feel I had contributed enough to the work to warrant co-authorship of the paper. It went off to a widely read journal under his name alone.

I was surprised to find that this signal success did not produce much of a transformation in Francis. I had expected that he would be cock-a-hoop, and that we would all see a great relaxation in his relations with other people. But, if anything, he was more tense than ever. The only light on the horizon was that I now occasionally saw him walking along the corridor with Jenny. Christopher, who no doubt had now got all he wanted out of Jenny, seemed no longer to be interested in her, and I thought it just possible that the news of Francis's discovery, which had, of course, spread through the department like wildfire, might have induced Jenny to take him more seriously. I didn't think that would do Jenny much good, but it would certainly have done wonders for Francis. Still, I must confess that I didn't really understand what it was that put Francis under such relentless pressure.

I found out quite by accident. I had come back to the laboratory late one Sunday afternoon to look at an experiment that I had going. There was usually nobody about at that time, and I was thus a little surprised to bump into Francis in the company of an old lady to whom he was explaining some of the photographs on our walls. He was obviously embarrassed to see me and endeavoured to escape, but I decided not to let him go and deliberately struck up a conversation, which left him no alternative but to introduce me to what I had already guessed was his mother. She was a small chubby person with a helmet of white hair set in a brittle permanent wave. Like Mrs Thatcher years later, she carried a large handbag on a strap.

She was only too pleased to talk to me. In fact, she was hard to stop. It was clear that Francis was the light of her life. His father had apparently died while Francis was still in arms, leaving mother and child in very difficult circumstances. It was only by the most heroic efforts that she had managed to give him an education, and I inferred from what she said that he must never have been allowed to forget the hopes that were pinned on him. I was happy to be able to assure her that Francis had done very well and that the paper he had just sent off was a contribution of great importance. Francis looked at his feet and squirmed, but his mother positively purred. She was able to assure me, in return, that Francis would undoubtedly continue to do well, as he had always been a very responsible boy and most diligent. I think she would have been perfectly content to go on giving me details about their life for as long as I cared to listen, but Francis's discomfiture was becoming so acute that I felt it was high time for me to extricate myself. So, at the next pause in the narrative, I told the good lady that it had been a great pleasure to talk to her and fled.

A few weeks before Francis's paper was sent off, I took on a new Ph.D. student. Stephanie seemed to me to be a very good prospect. Her undergraduate career had just those qualities that I like to see – something close to originality in those topics that caught her interest and relaxed competence in the rest. Moreover, her tutors made a point of mentioning that she had done particularly well in the practical classes. At interview, she had given evidence of possessing a good dose of the one thing that Francis lacked completely – a sense of humour. With Francis launched in a completely different direction, the problem that I had originally marked out for him now lacked an investigator. I still thought it a problem well worth investigating, and, with Francis's new enzyme assay, it was likely that rapid progress could be made. The idea appealed to Stephanie, and I asked Francis to show her exactly how the assay was done. About a month later I was surprised to find her still struggling with the assay, and I again asked Francis to help her with it. Another month went by, and then Stephanie asked to see me.

She seemed very embarrassed at what she had to say and said it with great reluctance, but what it boiled down to was that she couldn't get Francis's assay to work and didn't really believe that the assay, even in Francis's hands, could be trusted. Nonetheless, she was willing enough to go on working at it, but thought that the difficulties were unlikely to be resolved unless I could find the time to look into the assay myself. I spent most of the next couple of days with Stephanie. It quickly became clear that Francis's technique was nowhere near as reproducible as his elegant graphs made out. The measured levels of the two enzymes varied from experiment to experiment, not only in absolute terms but relative to each other, and one of them appeared to be strongly inhibited by an unidentified component present in some of the cell extracts. In our hands the whole thing was a mess. I went along to see Francis and told him that I had spent some time with Stephanie, who was still having difficulty with his assay, and that I hadn't made much headway with it myself. I didn't at all like it that he made a disparaging remark about Stephanie's competence and asked him to set aside a day in the next week or two to show me how to work the assay properly. But on the appointed day he failed to turn up and he was nowhere to be seen on the following day either. Since I no longer believed that he could possibly have solutions to all the problems we had encountered, I regarded his absence as ominous and made a snap decision to seek him out in his digs.

He had a room in a large Victorian house that seemed to be shared by about a dozen other students. One of them was sitting on the front steps drinking Coca Cola. He wore a T shirt that urged me to make love, not war. I asked him where Francis's room was and, to my surprise, he got up and guided me very courteously through the warren of corridors to his door. When I knocked, I was much relieved to hear Francis's voice asking me to come in. He was sitting in a battered armchair reading a small black gilt-edged book that I took to be a bible. He looked up at me, not with surprise or panic, but with an air of ineffable weariness. I told him that I had come because I thought he might be ill and perhaps in need of a little help. He was quick to tell me that he had indeed been unwell for the last few days but was feeling better now and hoped to return to work the following day. I could have left him at that point, but thought it risky to leave him to his own devices without giving him some form of reassurance, so I asked him whether he felt up to walking back to the laboratory with me, or at least part of the way. He seemed to welcome this suggestion, and that gave me the opportunity to let him see that I was not at all angry with him, but was, on the contrary, looking for some way to help him out of the desperate situation in which he had landed himself.

I explained that Stephanie and I were still very anxious to have his guidance, but if there were indeed some unresolved difficulties with the assay, it was vital that the publication of his paper be delayed. He seemed not to have grasped the fact that, with a claim of such importance, dozens of other scientists would take up his technique the moment the paper appeared, and if the technique was found wanting, his reputation would be irreparably damaged. I put it to him that it might be a good plan if I were to ring the editor of the journal to which the paper had been submitted and ask him to delay its publication until a complication that we had not foreseen was ironed out. He agreed at once. I then suggested that, as he had been unwell and had been working much too hard anyway, it might be a good idea if he took a little holiday. He could come along and have a chat with me after that.

I rang the editor the next day and explained the position. This editor was a rather stuffy individual, but he ran a good journal. I had to assure him that I was acting on Francis's behalf and that Francis would himself have made the request had he not been unwell. It appeared that we were in the nick of time, for the two referees to whom the paper had been sent for review, had both returned laudatory reports, and the paper was about to go to press. It didn't surprise me that the editor declined to hold the paper in abeyance. It would have to be withdrawn completely, he said, and re-submitted as a new paper when it was ready. This was a verdict that I was glad to accept.

When, a couple of weeks later, Francis came to see me, it was at once obvious that he had again undergone a profound change. I had wondered whether he would in fact come back and what I would be confronted with if he did. I had half expected a penitent plea to be given a second chance and had more or less decided that that wouldn't be a good idea, for it was now all too clear that Francis wasn't cut out for a career that entailed increasingly severe competition and frequent disappointment. Fortunately, the question did not arise. The Francis who came into my room was as near as he would ever get to being relaxed. He was wearing a new pair of blue jeans with a white turtle-necked shirt, and his hair was carefully combed back. He began by thanking me, with moving sincerity, for the trouble I had taken over him and then went on to say that, after a great deal of soul-searching, he had himself come to the conclusion that a life in research was not for him. He had apparently found the courage to confront his mother with a realistic appraisal of the situation in which he now found himself and had managed to get it through to her that he could no longer be the vehicle of her ambition. He told me he was thinking of applying for a job as a librarian in one of the big London science libraries and asked whether I would be willing to provide a reference for him. This seemed to me to be a splendid idea and I agreed, of course, to provide the reference. I never saw Francis again, but each Christmas he sends me a card on which he sometimes writes a few words in his unmistakable miniscule hand. That's how I learned that he had married, had produced a son and then a daughter, and was now in charge of the library that he had joined when he left me.

CHAPTER 6

PARIS IN THE SPRING

There was a time when medical students, as a matter of course, read the great classical works on which their science was based. Nowadays, all but a handful would regard it as a form of historical research to consult a paper that appeared five years ago. My generation fell somewhere in between. William Harvey, Louis Pasteur, Robert Koch and Claude Bernard have managed to find a place on my bookshelves. I am especially attached to my copy of Bernard's *Médecine Expérimentale*. It is the second edition, published in 1903 by Ch. Delagrave, 15 rue Soufflot, Paris. The volume is bound in calf, imprinted with modest gilt lettering, and at the base of the spine there are two initials, H. R. On the fly-leaf, a disciplined hand has written, in purple ink, Henri Richet, Nouméa. 1911.12.

I picked it up for a song almost forty years ago in one of the small secondhand bookshops that used then to thrive in some sort of symbiotic relationship with the university, and I have often wondered how the book managed to make its way here from Nouméa. I used to imagine that Henri Richet was a doctor in the French Colonial Service and that he had perhaps ordered the book from Paris in order to keep abreast of scientific developments in the metropolis. But the expensive binding and the beautiful purple handwriting suggested something more than a diligent practitioner doing his best in a remote Pacific island. Henri Richet must have known that the book was worth an expensive binding. There was a slim chance, I guess, that he might have been related to Charles Richet, who won the Nobel Prize for Physiology or Medicine in 1913 and for whom I felt a certain sympathy because he later endowed a prize of his own to reward distinguished literary work produced by doctors. I have read the book twice: once for the marvellous science that swept vitalism out of modern physiology, and once, much later, simply for the beauty of the language. But now, if that calf-bound volume happens to catch my eye, I do not think of Henri Richet, or Charles; I think of Véronique.

I first met Véronique Richet at a gathering of medievalists in one of our ancient colleges. You might well ask what I was doing there. Well, I suppose I must then confess that I have an argumentative interest – hopelessly amateurish, of course – in Roger Bacon, and Alan W., a medieval historian who is one of my oldest friends and who always treats my incursions into his territory with greater indulgence than they deserve, had suggested that I might like to hear a lecture entitled "Roger Bacon in Paris" that Véronique Richet was due to give at that meeting. For some now totally obscure reason, our highly technical departmental library contains a copy of the introduction that Bridges wrote for his edition of Bacon's *Opus Maius*, published separately in book form for a wider readership. A wet weekend and the ignominious collapse of some experiments I was working on presented me with an unexpected hiatus which that little volume neatly filled. I came away with the firm intention of finding out for myself whether it really was true, as Bridges had intimated, that this thirteenth century schoolman was a prescient forerunner of modern scientific method. When I had finished reading *On the Multiplication of Species* I came to the conclusion that he was not – a discovery that drove me to inflict on my colleagues a burst of unwanted commentary on the difference between medieval philosophy and modern science. I had never heard of Véronique Richet, but I knew that Alan would not have drawn her lecture to my attention unless he knew that it was going to be something out of the ordinary. So I went along.

She was a woman in her late forties, I should have thought, although it was difficult to tell, for she was one of those people who, having attained an elegant maturity, change very little with the passage of the years. She held her small spare frame rigidly erect, with shoulders thrown back in the manner that was no doubt thought appropriate for well brought up young ladies of an earlier generation. Her hair, which must once have been very fair, was now shot through with silver and was drawn smoothly back into a chignon. I still have a vivid picture of what she wore that day even though almost three decades have since gone by: an autumnal brown tweed suit which could well have been sold in Paris as something quintessentially English but which had about it a stylishness that was unmistakably French, a simple white blouse tied at the neck with a ribbon that matched the colour of her tweeds, and sensible brogues ideal for walking on our worn cobbles.

She began her lecture in French, not the high-speed effervescent French of contemporary Paris, but the sort of speech I could imagine hearing in the circle of the Guermantes – polished and precise, with every possible liaison carefully made. After two or three minutes, however, she announced that she proposed to give the rest of the lecture in English, this being the native language of most of the participants at the conference, and she asked for a little forbearance. It was not needed. She spoke fluent and highly idiomatic English, with just enough of a Gallic accent to confer an added charm to what she was saying. To my great delight, she summarily dismissed the notion that Bacon was any kind of a scientist in the modern sense, and placed him squarely in the mainstream of thirteenth century scholasticism. Her knowledge of Bacon's philosophical work was profound, and her assessment of its significance entirely convincing, but her lecture would have been better entitled "The Paris of Roger Bacon", for it was the medieval city itself, its people, its buildings, its books, its daily life, that formed the centrepiece of what she had to say. Bacon was the peg on which she hung her dazzling tapestry. When she finished, she was given the closest that academics get to a standing ovation.

Later that day I received a telephone call from Alan asking me whether I could manage dinner at his home the following evening. He had invited Véronique and a couple of other visitors from overseas. Véronique turned up in a stunning 'petite robe noire' which set off her silvering hair to perfection. Alan gave me the pleasure of sitting next to her at dinner, and after we had exchanged the usual civilities, I asked her the question that had been running through my mind from the moment I first heard her name. Was she perhaps related to an Henri Richet who had lived in Nouméa before the first World War? "But of course!" she exclaimed, "My uncle! How amazing that you should know anything about him." I confessed that I knew nothing about him except that he had written his name and Nouméa 1911.12. in purple ink in a copy of Bernard's *Médecine Expérimentale* that I now owned. "Ah", she chuckled, "then we were obviously destined to meet!" And so, at long last, I learned that Henri Richet was not a doctor in the French Colonial Service, but a writer who had enjoyed a moment of celebrity in Paris and then, taking a leaf out of Gauguin's book, had fled to a Pacific island to seek tranquillity and inspiration. Véronique had no idea why he had ordered *La Médecine Expérimentale* from Paris (we agreed that it was most improbable that it would have been for sale in Nouméa in 1911), but she suspected that it might have been an interest in Bergson and the philosophy of vitalism that had prompted the purchase. In any case, she was sure that Henri, unlike Charles to whom he was in fact distantly related, knew nothing about physiology or, for that matter, any other science. He had returned to Paris towards the end of a wandering life and died there. Perhaps some member of our university, on a trip to France, had bought Henri's calf-bound volume from a Paris bouquiniste.

I had Véronique to myself for much of the evening. The other two guests were a voluble Texan, who was attempting to use computational methods to obtain a better idea of the structure of medieval town populations, and an elderly professor of Germanic studies from Heidelberg who had written a standard work on the minnesingers. The Texan was bubbling over with enthusiasm for an approach to medieval history that had many of the elements of what later became transiently fashionable under the name of cliometrics, but Véronique was more than sceptical. A life spent in the study of medieval documents had made it abundantly clear to her that the fragmentary nature of the primary sources would never support such complex numerical treatment. So there was hardly a meeting of minds there, and as for the German professor, the war was still too close for Véronique to be on easy terms with a man who had held his professorship without hindrance throughout the whole of the Nazi period. (Alan told me later that during the German occupation of Paris, Véronique had been involved in various clandestine operations and had been remarkably lucky to escape capture.) So the Texan turned his guns on the German professor and I took my courage in my hands and talked about Roger Bacon with Véronique.

The following day I showed her round the oldest remnants of the medieval university and, in the light of her comments, saw them for the first time in a context of a larger European cultural movement and, more particularly, as a repercussion of the intellectual ferment that was then emanating from Paris. About a week later, I received the first of many letters written in her immaculate italic hand. She thanked me for the trouble I had taken in showing her so many interesting things and insisted that on my next visit to Paris I should get in touch with her.

That visit came off about a year later. I had been asked to give a lecture at an international conference that was due to take place there in the middle of May. I didn't dislike international conferences as much then as I do now, and Paris in the spring was, in any case, irresistible. It was the first international conference in my subject to be held in France since the war, so there was the added inducement of perhaps making contact with French scientists whom I then knew only by name. The meetings were to be held at the Centre Universitaire in the Grand Palais, and block bookings had been made for overseas participants in a number of nearby hotels. But that wasn't the part of Paris for which I had much affection.

I am not greatly moved by architecture whose primary function is to impress, and I like triumphal architecture even less. The Champs-Elysées, Trafalgar Square, the Siegesallee and the Rajpath leave me cold. I made my booking in a small hotel on the other side of the river in the rue Madame, close by the Place St Sulpice. I had stayed there before and particularly liked the fact that the proprietress had managed to bring the plumbing up to date without debauching the traditionally Parisian character of the establishment. My greatest pleasure in Paris is to stroll, without purpose, along the old streets of the Left Bank, and in the rue Madame that pleasure was on my doorstep.

I arrived quite late in the evening and went straight to bed. During the night there must have been quite a bit of rain, although I didn't hear it, for when I looked out of my windows in the morning the sun was dancing in the puddles on the pavement and the whole city gleamed like a jewel. After the grande crème and the croissant, accompanied, as always, by a whiff of Gauloise Bleue, I decided that I would walk across the city to the Grand Palais in order to say hello once again to the streets that I had come to regard as old friends. I didn't take the shortest route, but ambled down past the ancient church of St-Germain-des-Prés, took the rue Jacob as far as the Faculté de Médecine, and then turned into the rue des Saints-Pères. In those days, the rue des Saints-Pères was not beset by a constant stream of traffic and you could still stroll gently down to the quais stopping now and then to examine the window display of an antique shop or a small art gallery. I stayed on the Left Bank as far as the Pont Alexandre III, and then crossed the river.

The conference began with an address by some dignitary from the Ministry of Education. He spoke in French but added a few words in English at the end. This appeared to set the style for almost all the French participants, who either spoke entirely in French or began in French and finished in English. For everyone else, English was already the scientific lingua franca. The opening plenary lecture was given by a voice from the past. The old man had been the foremost French biologist of his day, but his day was long before the war and I, for one, was surprised to learn that he was still alive. On the dais, a small table and a small wooden chair had been prepared for him and, in the time-honoured tradition of the Sorbonne, he sat down to lecture. He put his notes on the table in front of him but once he had begun he hardly glanced at them. He was making a point: that chair and that table were the lineal descendants of the 'chaire' and the 'pupitre', that had been devised by the clercs of Paris in the thirteenth century. He did not propose to let his audience forget how much they owed to France.

His lecture was unforgettable. Of course, he had no more than a nodding acquaintance with the dramatic developments that had taken place in biology since the war, but he had a long clear view of his subject and he expounded it in elegant French prose. I have always found the French perspective on the history of biology a refreshing change from the authorised versions of the subject – all very similar – that have appeared in English. Figures that receive barely a mention in our histories are often given prominence by French historians who see them not only as influences in their own time, but also as seminal determinants of subsequent developments. This alternative view is often dismissed by those who have not given it a moment's thought as a form of chauvinism, but I have not found chauvinism to be the exclusive prerogative of any one nation. He spoke for precisely forty-five minutes, as the programme announced that he would, then he gathered up the notes he had scarcely looked at, got up from his chair, bowed once, ever so slightly, and walked off. It was a performance that should have brought the house down, but there was no more than a brief and meagre sputter of applause. Most of his audience hadn't understood one word of what he said.

Luckily, my own lecture had been scheduled for that first morning, so that when I had given it I could regard myself as having done my duty and could feel free to pass my time more agreeably than in listening to the recitation of scientific material I had already read or trading scientific gossip in the corridors. I had written to Véronique to let her know that I was coming and had suggested that I would ring her at an opportune moment to see whether she could perhaps again spare an hour or two on furthering my education. When she answered the telephone that evening she seemed genuinely pleased to hear from me (not, I think, just conceit on my part or politeness on hers) and volunteered the following afternoon for a glimpse of Gothic Paris. When I asked whether she was free to have dinner with me after that, she explained, a little hesitantly, that she was not free that evening but, in the hope that I could come, had invited a few friends to dinner at her home the next day.

We began with the Musée de Cluny, then walked down that ancient thoroughfare, the rue St Jacques, to St Séverin, and crossed over to the Ile de la Cité by the Petit Pont. I had visited the Musée de Cluny only once before and only cursorily at that. I didn't remember that it had a garden and wouldn't have attached any importance to the portal at its entrance even if I had noticed it at all. For Véronique that portal was the key to the medieval history of the whole area – the last vestige of the Chapelle de la Sainte Vierge that had once formed part of the original buildings of the abbey of Saint-Germain-des-Prés. She explained how it had come about that the abbots of Cluny had built their town house on the site at the beginning of the fourteenth century and how this medieval rarity had eventually been resurrected as a museum. And in the museum itself she did not attempt to take me on a guided tour, but picked out no more than a dozen or so of the exhibits – all masterpieces –

and used each of them as the starting point of a journey into the daily life that had generated it.

Véronique obviously had a special affection for Saint Séverin and thought it as beautiful as any of the gothic buildings in Paris. I do not have an eye sensitive to restorations, once they have weathered, or to later additions if they are skillfully done, but for Véronique the thirteenth and the fifteenth centuries were aeons apart, and she picked the old church to pieces for me as easily as if she were separating chalk from cheese. Her commentary on the carvings of the south wall was a revelation, and I have never again looked at medieval carving without thinking back to what she made me see for the first time that day. She assumed I knew all about Nôtre Dame, which was far from true, and we darted in just for a moment so that she could show me a point of similarity between one of the carvings on the choir screen and what I had just seen on the wall of Saint Séverin. It was the Sainte Chapelle that she made for, hoping that we would see it before the sun got too low, for it was dwarfed by the surrounding Palais de Justice which shut out the afternoon sun much too soon and extinguished the magic of the light that filtered through the stained glass windows. We were not too late, and Véronique was able to take me gently through the subtleties of that ornate royal chapel in all its iridescent splendour. We finished the day on a bench in the square du Vert Galant on the tip of the island, resting our tired legs and watching the sun disappear through the iron struts of the Pont des Arts.

Véronique' s flat was in an old house in the rue de la Montagne-Sainte-Geneviève, a stone's throw from the Place Maubert. All the guests were already at their aperitifs when I arrived having grossly misjudged how long it would take to get across Paris at peak hour. Jacques B. I had met once before when he visited our university to give a lecture which, as I recall it, was entitled "Mach, Boltzmann and the Reality of Atoms". He was one of Europe's most distinguished particle physicists and I had found his lecture deeply impressive, not only because of his remarkable ability to present complex, and essentially mathematical, ideas in a form that was readily comprehensible to the uninitiated, but also because he was able to handle the philosophical and the physical implications of the Mach-Boltzmann controversy over the reality of atoms with equal mastery. He was a tall, thin man with long slender fingers which were constantly at play as he talked, and a face that bore a striking resemblance to the image that we have of Voltaire. His wife, Simone, was small and dark with infinitely sad brown eyes. She, being Jewish, was the compelling reason for their having fled to England when France collapsed in 1940. During the war, he became an influential figure in the entourage of Charles de Gaulle. It was at this dinner that I first met Jean-Paul d' A., then an elegant young man still undecided whether to devote his life to the study of Marcel Proust or to the analysis of cell structure. A couple of years later he came to work in my laboratory, but the tension between science and literature remained unresolved. I don't think it ever was resolved. I knew about Philomène T., or Philo, as they all called her, for there had been a Profile of her in one of our papers shortly after she'd won a literary prize of some sort for a novel, as I remember it, with an unusually realistic Caribbean background. She was a strikingly attractive antillaise, originally from Martinique, but she now had an academic position in Paris and was close to completing a serious book on the development of Creole dialects.

It appeared that my arrival had interrupted a lively exchange of views about the structure of academic institutions in France. I was drawn into it by Jean-Paul, who asked me whether I agreed with him that the whole thing should be blown to smithereens. I confessed that I didn't know enough about it to have an opinion, so, for my benefit, he went on to paint a picture of self-centred, brittle, archaic, and even corrupt, practices that I found difficult to believe. But, to my surprise, neither Véronique nor Jacques, although they laughed a little at Jean-Paul's exaggerations, actually disagreed with him. They were all agreed that major reforms had to be made, and if they were not made soon the whole system would be brought down by student agitation. What worried Jean-Paul most was the way in which French science had isolated itself almost deliberately from the rest of the world. "Do you know, Henri," he said "that you cannot be appointed to a teaching position in a French university unless you have a French doctorate? A doctorate from your university won't do. So young French scientists don't dare go abroad for their doctoral work, but are forced to work under the supervision of opinionated old dinosaurs who ruin them for life". Once again,

Véronique and Jacques did not disagree even though, in Jean-Paul's eyes, they must have belonged to the generation of the dinosaurs. "The real problem" Simone interjected "is that the French academic establishment and French ministers continue to behave as if France still occupied the position of dominance that it had in the world of learning before the Franco-Prussian war, whereas, in many respects, ours has become a provincial culture." I told them about the splendid opening lecture at the conference I was supposed to be attending and how, for the great majority of the audience, it was totally incomprehensible. "Ah yes," said Jacques "the defence of the French language. You know, we are under great pressure to make our presentations in French whenever we go to lecture abroad and to publish our important work in French journals even though they are not widely read even in France. Ministers seem to think that you can force the French language on the outside world. Of course, the only way to save the French language as an international medium for scholarly communication is for us to produce science and literature of such high quality that the rest of the world will be obliged to read what we write. And that, with one or two notable exceptions, we are not doing."

Véronique demurred a little at this and claimed that in her subject she had no difficulty in being understood when she lectured in French, although she always endeavoured, as a matter of courtesy, to lecture in the language that was most familiar to her audience insofar as that lay within her power. "That" said Jacques "is no more than a transitional phase. Once the science becomes decadent, it is only a matter of time until the humanities become decadent also. Then you won't be understood when you lecture in French either."

However, it was Philo who had the last word. "For all of you" she said "this is a matter of prestige, *amour-propre*, national pride. But for me the French language is something else altogether. It is a lifeline. When I was a child I lived with my mother and grandmother at Trois-Ilets, and each day I would take the little ferryboat over the bay to my school in Fort de France. I used to prepare my lessons during the crossing, for there was little time or opportunity to do much at home. Bossuet and Fénelon under a Caribbean sun. Can you imagine? And that pathetic little collection of French classics in our brilliantly decorated Schoelcher public library. If it were not for them, I would now be working as a waitress in one of our expensive tourist hotels and would be obliged to take a shower each morning before I went on duty so that my body odour did not offend the guests."

But Veronique's excellent blanquette de veau and a subversive Volnay made short work of our academic preoccupations, and soon it was all laughter and gossip and, from Véronique, hilarious anecdotes of student life in Paris before the war. When the dinner was over, Philo, in a gentle contralto, let us have "Ba moin an tibo" and then that lovely old lament, "Adieu foulard, adieu madras".

Almost exactly two years after the student revolution of 1968 had torn the French university system, and much else, apart, I was again in Paris in the middle of May. This time it wasn't an international conference, but an invitation to lecture at one of the 'séances hebdomadaires' of the Académie des Sciences. The 'Comptes rendus' of these weekly meetings of the Academy used once to be avidly read by scientists everywhere, but since the war hardly anyone in the English-speaking world looked at them. But Pasteur and Bernard had presented their experiments at these weekly meetings, and that was enough to induce me to prepare my lecture with more than usual care and to prepare it in French.

Let me tell you something of the room in which these meetings are held. It is the 'grande salle des seances' of the Institut de France, that slightly intimidating domed structure that looks out across the Seine to the Louvre. The room is made available to other academies by the Académie Française, and you reach it from the vestibule by passing through the 'salon de conversation' where splendid eighteenth century paintings adorn the walls and where the 'immortals' themselves sometimes gather after their own meetings. The 'grande salle des séances' is, by modern standards, small and cramped with worn seats arranged round three sides of a rectangle. The lecturer stands at the centre of this seating plan, at the same level as his audience, which gives you the feeling that you are having a friendly conversation with interested colleagues rather than delivering a formal lecture. I don't suppose much had changed since Pasteur and Bernard described their findings to a similar gathering. I am not by nature a traditionalist, but I couldn't help being immensely pleased that the revolution of 1968 hadn't brought everything to the ground.

86

That evening, I was taken to a relaxed dinner at the Méditerranée, that delightful restaurant near the Odéon where Jean Cocteau had decorated the walls.

The following morning I rang Véronique and asked whether I could take her out to dinner. I wanted to make an occasion of it, and proposed Taillevent, but she thought that much too grand and suggested instead a bistro-cum-restaurant a short walk from her home. I was a little disappointed, but of course agreed. I had heard that she had taken early retirement, but could only guess at what might have precipitated such an improbable development. I arrived at the bistro first and was gazing at the front door when she entered. I had always regarded her as essentially ageless, but what confronted me now was an old lady. Nothing fundamental had changed. She still held herself erect and threw her shoulders back, but her hair was now quite white and her face showed deep lines that I hadn't before noticed. And every now and then, as she spoke, she would sigh a little, as if she were very tired. The bistro was run by a talkative couple from Lyons who provided what has now become a rarity in Paris – unpretentious but excellent French bourgeois cuisine. Once again Véronique' s judgement had been sounder than mine. We decided to share a carré d' agneau des prés salants and a bottle of the Volnay to which she remained faithful.

They say revolutions eat their children. Well, she hadn't exactly been a child of the revolution but she had supported it. Unlike some of her colleagues, she didn't join the students at the barricades, but she had long believed that drastic changes in the French university system were essential and that a student revolt was inevitable if they were not made. Curiously enough for someone so steeped in history, she overlooked the fact that what issues from revolutions bears little relationship to the aims or ideals of the revolutionaries. It wasn't long before questions began to be asked about the relevance (whatever that might mean) of what she taught. She took the view that in a civilized society scholarship did not require justification and certainly not in terms of relevance to anything else. Then she was put under strong pressure to produce simplified lecture notes that summarised in an organised way the minimum amount of information that the students would be expected to assimilate. Her reaction to this was to spell out, in no uncertain terms, that she was teaching in a university and not a primary school. Then she was showered with demands that her course be completely "re-structured" so that it could be fully understood by those with no Latin. She replied that the history of medieval Europe could not be studied without Latin. So she, of all people, became the arch-reactionary, the focus of polemical abuse in the student press. When she resigned, only a handful of her colleagues had offered their commiserations and none had supported her in her stand.

"Did I ever tell you, Henri" she went on to say "that I worked with Marc Bloch during those few years he had here at the Sorbonne before the war? And they want me to teach medieval history without Latin!" "Was it true" I asked "that he had shouted 'Vive la France!' in the face of the German firing squad?" "Oh yes," she replied "it's quite true. There were eye-witnesses who survived. I would have done the same had they caught me. But I don't much feel like shouting 'Vive la France!' now." It was a wonderful warm evening and we decided to walk back to her flat by a circuitous route. As we approached the Place Maubert, she remarked that the old cobbles had now been covered with asphalt. "I wonder", she mused "what the next generation of students will throw at the police now that the cobbles have been tarred over".

Several years went by before I next had an occasion to make an academic visit to Paris. I had almost ceased to attend international conferences and had reluctantly agreed to give the opening lecture at this one only because one of its principal sponsors was a good friend and a man whom I greatly admired. There was by then no question of giving an opening lecture at an international scientific conference in any language other than English, but I decided nonetheless to make my usual gesture to my Parisian hosts, and gave the first few minutes of my talk in French. This provoked a good deal of restlessness in the audience. Several pairs of heads came together in audible whispers and there was a widespread shuffling of feet. I suppose many thought that I was simply showing off. Things settled down when I moved into English, but I couldn't help wondering as I made the transition what would have happened if I had attempted to give the whole of my lecture in French. I found out later that day. One of the communications in the afternoon programme bore a French title. It was to be given by one of the most promising of the younger generation of French biologists, and I went along to hear what he had to say. He had indeed decided to speak in French, and he had hardly got under way when a group of brash young Americans, unmistakable in dress and manner, simply got up and walked out. And, as incomprehension gave way to impatience, their example was followed by others. By the time the lecture was over, two-thirds of the audience had already disappeared.

When I got back to my hotel (still in the rue Madame and, mercifully, little changed), there was a message from Jean-Paul asking me to ring him. Paris, he explained, was an awful place with motor cars all over the pavements. He was thinking of driving out to Auvers-sur-Oise for a civilised meal the following day. Would I like to come? We arranged to meet at his flat in mid-afternoon so that we could get out of Paris before the peak hour traffic built up and perhaps manage to visit Vincent Van Gogh's grave before it got dark. Jean-Paul's flat was in the Boulevard Haussman with front windows that looked out on the house in which Proust had lived for more than a decade. Proust now seemed to dominate his imagination, for two of the rooms were lined with cork and the whole place was stuffed with bric-a-brac from the *belle epoque*. He spent half an hour explaining the relevance of some of these objects to Proust and his circle, and then we set off.

As we sped through the Paris suburbs and out into the country, I reminded him of the happy evening we had had, ages ago it now seemed, at Véronique's flat in the rue de la Montagne-St-Geneviève. I knew that Véronique had died the year before because there had been an obituary notice in the only one of our newspapers that takes any interest in the intellectual life of other countries. "A whole host of her former academic colleagues turned up at the funeral" Jean-Paul informed me "and many of them must have had a pretty guilty conscience. She lies with her ancestors in the family crypt at Père-Lachaise". "And what about Jacques B., Simone, and Philo?" I asked. Jean-Paul seemed to know exactly what they were all doing. Jacques had been the centre of a great deal of attention in the French press two or three years previously. A Nobel Prize in physics had been awarded to two Americans whose work, in the judgement of many people, depended heavily on theories developed earlier by Jacques. Several of his colleagues had written letters of protest to the

Paris newspapers which had been only too eager to take up his cause. Needless to say, Jacques refused to utter a word. He had now retired from his professorship and had bought a small farmhouse a few miles out of Grasse. That's where he and Simone now seemed to spend all their time. Jacques was writing a history of particle physics (no doubt from a Gallic point of view), and Simone, who, I now heard for the first time, was a talented sculptor, was doing some interesting heads that had recently been exhibited in Paris. But Philo, it appeared, had become disenchanted with Paris and had gone back to Martinique. She had completed her book on Creole dialects and had written another Caribbean novel which had been well received but hadn't been taken up by the press as much as her first book. Still, with the help of a little journalism, she had felt able to support herself by her pen and had followed her nostalgia back to Trois-Ilets. Jean-Paul thought she was something of a cult figure in Martinique.

It had been a typical April day, with pale sunshine and intermittent showers, but as we drove into Auvers, the late afternoon sun came out quite strongly and a little mist began to rise from the wet fields. The inn in which Van Gogh ended his life still functioned as a restaurant, and from the way in which the 'patron' greeted him I guessed that Jean-Paul must have been a pretty regular customer. The little attic room that Van Gogh had occupied was not then normally open to the public, but Jean-Paul had little difficulty in gaining access to it. You went up two flights of narrow stairs and there it was, quite bare except for an iron bedstead and a wooden chair with a rush seat, just like the one that he had painted. Through the tiny window you could see a cloud drifting by. Jean-Paul told the chef what we wanted for dinner but explained that we intended to visit the grave first. So we walked up the gentle slope beside the cemetery and found the two identical gravestones, Vincent's and Theo's, side by side. As you look down on the village from the cemetery you can see the church and the houses that Vincent had painted in his last mad days, and in the half-light a flock of crows came wheeling down over the fields, menacing against a darkening sky.

The following morning I decided to visit another grave. The sky was grey and the streets wet with drizzle. It was the sort of day that

Caillebotte had caught perfectly in his wonderful painting of Paris in the rain. The bus ride out to Ménilmontant was slow and dreary, and it was only after a lot of wandering about in the wet that I found what I was looking for. The Richet family crypt was an ornate, and I thought rather ugly, structure in the older part of the cemetery. It must have been erected in the middle of the nineteenth century and was now very neglected. A wrought iron gate precluded entry beyond a certain point but I could make out the inscriptions on the stone plaques that had not yet worn away. In one corner I found an intricately carved plaque that marked the final abode of Henri Richet, who, in Nouméa in 1911, had written his name in purple ink in what is now my copy of Bernard's *Médecine Expérimentale*, and in another a much smaller and very simple plaque for Véronique Francine Richet with nothing on it but the year of her birth and the year of her death. It was quite new, of course, but it was already covered with grime.

CHAPTER 7

DEAD WOOD

There are scientists, often powerful on committees, whose main aim in life seems to be the elimination of dead wood. Their enthusiasm for this exercise must, I suppose, rest on the assumption that they are not themselves dead wood, an assumption not always shared by their colleagues. K. was a typical specimen of the genre, but I have to admit that in some respects his career was a phenomenon. I don't think that anything that he himself ever did in the way of an experiment turned out to be substantially correct, but he was none-theless appointed to a professorship of biochemistry at an early age and his influence continued to grow from year to year, despite the mediocrity of the research that he was supposed to be directing and ample evidence of poor judgement. I think the main factor in his early success was that his hair was prematurely grey, which gave his utterances a weight that their content would not otherwise have supported. When he lectured to biochemists, he concentrated on the clinical applications of his work; and when he spoke to clinicians he stuck to biochemistry. In this way he managed to evade robust criticism and, indeed, received a good deal of praise as a facilitator of communication between the two groups. He was, I must admit, a good expositor, although there was always a certain glibness in his manner that irritated me, and he seemed quite unable (or unwilling) to present data in the modest and circumspect manner that I regarded as the hallmark of a serious scientist. But if his style didn't suit me, it suited the media to a T. His handsome impressive head and his talent for over-simplification were just what the makers of television programmes were looking for, and he was often to be seen laying down the law on a variety of subjects that I would not have regarded as lying within his competence. Indeed, he eventually became the authority to whom journalists would normally turn if they wanted comment on some new medical or biological development.

However, it was not only on the general public that he exerted influence. Largely with the support of clinicians, for whom he constituted a rare source of comprehensible biochemistry, he managed to find his way onto a number of committees that controlled the flow of funds into medical research. I once served with him on one of these committees, and although I naturally disagreed with most of what he had to say, there was no denying that he was very effective. He always waited until one or two of the other members had spoken and then delivered his verdict a little hesitantly and with a furrowed brow, as if he had worried a great deal about the matter in hand and had come to his decision only after weighing the pros and cons with the utmost care. He was certainly very diligent in preparing the items that he was asked to comment on, and there was no detail in the voluminous papers that escaped his attention. But what he came out with was little more than a recitation of the received wisdom, and when a genuine difficulty arose, that received wisdom almost always led to the wrong conclusions.

I found his reaction to grant applications that lay within the field of his own research particularly obnoxious. He never said that an application was not worth supporting, but simply volunteered the information that if he were investigating the problem, he would approach it in a completely different way and adopt a much more sophisticated version of the appropriate technology. Since most of the other members of the committee were not experts in the field, his technical comments served to reinforce his position as the final arbiter on all such applications and usually resulted in their not being funded or, at least, being funded at a lower level than they merited. What incensed me most about K.'s technical comments was the knowledge that much of the work that issued from his own department was technically incompetent, but it was, of course, completely impossible for me to say this, or even hint at it at the committee meetings.

I also had the strong impression that K. must have made deals with other members of the committee before our meetings took place. It was the convention that you left the room when an application from your own institution was being considered, but I was astonished to find that a huge, and in my view implausible, application from K.'s department won strong support from members of the committee who, I was perfectly sure, must have seen straight through it.

On later occasions, I observed K. duly repaying the debt. He was particularly hard, in his circumspect way, on those at the beginning and those at the end of their scientific careers. He rarely took a chance on a young scientist who had yet to make his mark unless he happened to be located in one of the large laboratories that was already receiving substantial support. "You can't do science on your own any more" he would argue. "It's simply throwing money down the drain to encourage a beginner to go it alone in the wilderness." And even the most distinguished experimentalist, striking a dry patch in a hitherto exemplary career, was "dead wood" to K. "In the present financial climate we have to be ruthless" he expounded. "We must put our money behind the big battalions." I never fully understood why he was so obsessed with eliminating dead wood, but found it difficult to avoid the suspicion that at least part of his motivation was the desire to remove from the scene elements that he knew would be ranged against him. I was convinced that if the administration of our science came to be dominated by people like K., there would soon be little science left worth talking about.

You will now understand my consternation when I heard that K. had been included in the visiting group that was due to review one of the research programmes in my own department and, in particular, the work of Michael S. Michael was a lifelong friend and, in his own idiosyncratic way, one of the most gifted individuals I had ever met. We had been Ph.D. students together, and although the problem he was working on was not closely related to mine, I was forever consulting him about one thing or another, for his intellectual range was immense and he was all too generous with his time. He had been the foremost classicist at his school, which was famous for its precocious classicists, and when he came up to our university with an open scholarship, it was with the intention of reading classics. But after a few weeks an over-riding interest in butterflies induced him to turn to biology where he quickly assimilated what he hadn't done at school and proceeded to display in examinations the dazzling virtuosity that had previously characterised his work in classics.

Usually, when an undergraduate in the humanities makes the transition to science, he has great difficulty with the mathematical aspects of the work. But there was no such problem for Michael. It soon transpired that he was a natural mathematician, and could just as easily have offered mathematics at the university entrance examinations if he hadn't been coerced into classics by the tradition of his school. Michael's transition to science coincided with the revolution in biology unleashed by the elucidation of the chemical structure of genes, and he was quick to realise that the questions that had aroused his interest in butterflies would not be answered by field work in the Darwinian tradition. So he turned his attention to the deep end of genetics, the physico-chemical end that most biologists cannot penetrate. There can have been very few of his contemporaries who had mastered what was then the cutting edge of biology so completely. On graduation, he was at once elected into a fellowship at his college, and was already a minor celebrity in the university when we first met as Ph.D. students.

Let me now say that there was nothing forbidding about the bearer of this remarkable intellect. He had a freckled, mischievous face that was incompatible with any measure of gravity and a mop of reddish hair that tended to fall down over his forehead. I think he generally regarded academic pursuits, indeed life in general, as something of a game, and several times in the course of every day I would hear his high pitched laughter pealing down the corridor. His approach to problems or, for that matter, to people, had an irrepressible playfulness about it that was not at all a pose, but an essential component of his personality. He thought nothing of abandoning his work in the middle of the day to see a film he was interested in, or of going off to London for a week if he felt bored. This aristocratic detachment would, of course, have been nothing out of the ordinary in an earlier age when laboratories were peopled by gentleman-scientists, but it was a notably eccentric lifestyle by the time Michael and I began our careers.

There was always an element of tension between Michael and his

Ph.D. supervisor, who had a rather puritan view of the moral virtue of consistent hard work, but since Michael's idle interludes were almost always followed by developments that showed real flair, the uneasy truce between the two incompatibles held. Of course, there's a good deal of scholastic drudge in every Ph.D. programme, and while a plausible argument can be made that this drudge is a discipline worth undergoing at least once in one's life, it was not an argument that cut much ice with Michael. His Ph.D. work produced two important papers, to which his supervisor was very pleased to add his name, but when it came to writing the thesis, Michael turned in a careless, even flippant, document that was referred back for extensive revision. Michael's first reaction to this was simply not to bother, but for reasons that came perilously close to *noblesse oblige*, he did in the end make the necessary corrections and was awarded his Ph.D. degree.

The head of our department at that time had a keen nose for talent, and although he didn't much care for Michael's style either, he thought him too gifted to be allowed to escape. So Michael stayed on in the laboratory and combined sporadic bursts of experimental work with the pleasures and chores of collegiate life. But that wasn't all he did. He was an excellent cellist and became the mainstay of an almost professional string quartet, and when some subject, in the humanities as well as in the sciences, caught his interest, he could write about it with astonishing insight. He never became a dominant figure in the international scientific scene. That would have called for a degree of consistency that he was unable, or perhaps unwilling, to provide, but his views were always treated with great respect and, on two occasions separated by a period of about ten years, he had made contributions of the first importance, in both cases by solving a problem that had defied everyone else. He greeted my appointment to the headship of the department with unfeigned pleasure, for he was not in the least competitive and, in any case, would never have agreed to take on the burdens of the post had he been offered it. I can't tell you how much I owe Michael for the help he has given me over the years.

Michael's research was not an expensive item in anyone's budget. He was more than satisfied with one or two collaborators, and they worked more with their heads than with their hands. I shouldn't have thought there was any point in sending a visiting group to review his work. His relaxed independence was widely known (and envied), but then so were his contributions to science, infrequent though they may have been. No textbook of molecular biology failed to make reference to discoveries that he had made. Had he been Japanese, he might well have been classified as a National Treasure and encouraged, with the deepest respect, to do whatever he chose. The organizations that now finance our research do not operate on so elevated a plane; indeed their prevailing ethos can only with difficulty be distinguished from that of bank clerks. Since it was normal practice to send visiting groups from time to time to inspect all recipients of long term support, nobody apparently saw any reason to treat Michael differently, so a small team of inspectors that included K. was assembled and a date fixed for the visit. It came at a very bad time, for Michael had published nothing of any scientific consequence for almost five years.

The visit was a disaster. Michael thought nothing of the inspectors and, uncharacteristically, let is show. He told me later that K. had had the effrontery to ask him what he had been doing for the last five years, to which Michael had answered, with his customary flippancy, that he had been waiting for inspiration. Pressed by K. to elaborate a little on this, Michael had made no effort to reduce his exposition to a level that K. might have understood, and since he always talked about his work in a disparaging, self-deprecatory, way, it was not hard to imagine what kind of impression he must have made. Still, I didn't believe that there was any real possibility that his grant would not be renewed. But about a month later he came to see me, waving a letter that he had just received. It was signed by some minor official who informed him in stiff bureaucratic language that, although the visiting group had found some of his work interesting, they could not, in the present financial circumstances, recommend that support be continued beyond the expiration of his present grant. I exploded, but Michael, apparently unruffled, simply said "Well, maybe they're right, Henry. Maybe I am washed up as a scientist." I made him promise me that he would not be deflected one whit by the obtuse decision of the visiting group, and I promised him that I would find support for his work from some other source. I was confident that I could keep my promise, but I wondered whether he would be able to keep his. When, in a belated endeavour to make light of the whole business, I tossed in the observation that his work cost next to nothing anyway, he had replied "That's because it's worth next to nothing." I cannot say that he seemed particularly despondent when he left my room, but many weeks went by before I saw him in the laboratory again.

About a year after the visiting group's inspection, we were all startled to read on the front page of one of our daily papers a headline that read NEW HOPE OF CURE FOR BREAST CANCER. It appeared that K. had announced at a press conference, convened for the purpose, that scientists in his group had isolated from the surface of breast cancer cells a molecule of great promise. K. was reported to be claiming that analysis of the structure of this molecule would permit a whole new family of drugs to be designed with the highly desirable property of being able to kill cancer cells while leaving normal cells unscathed. I assumed that this was the usual drivel that operators like K. generate in the press from time to time to capture attention and, of course, funds. But this particular item of news was less ephemeral than most. The theme was taken up by other newspapers, and later that week I saw K. on television giving a slightly more intelligible version of what his group had achieved. It is well known that some breast cancers need certain hormones in order to grow. If you remove these hormones in various ways, or prevent them from acting, you can sometimes stop the growth of the cancer or greatly retard it. The molecule on the surface of the cell to which the hormone attaches, and which is essential for its function, is called a 'receptor', and what K. claimed was that in addition to the receptor present on normal breast cells, cancer cells had an additional receptor that was not found on any normal cell. If this was true, it was certainly a spectacular finding and would indeed attract worldwide attention to this new molecule and to the possibility of designing drugs that would interact specifically with it.

Although K.'s previous record did not encourage confidence in what he was now touting, it had to be admitted that even the most mediocre scientists are sometimes lucky and, in all innocence, have important discoveries thrust upon them. I asked Michael what he thought of the story, but he declined to make any comment until he had seen the work in print. The paper appeared, in a rushed form and with K.'s name in the prime position, a few weeks later. It didn't seem too convincing to me, but I was no expert in that field and again asked Michael what he thought. He threw back his head, laughed, and tossed me a bit of Juvenal – "Verbosa et grandis epistola ..." Michael's scepticism was not however shared by those who determined the flow of funds for cancer research, for I heard shortly afterwards that K. had received another huge grant to enable him to exploit his new discovery. But it wasn't personal animosity that moved Michael to look more closely at K.' s findings. He knew as much as anybody about receptors on cell surfaces, but he wasn't engaged in experiments of that kind when K.'s paper appeared. In fact, I wasn't sure exactly what he was doing, for he was not often to be seen in the laboratory, and when he did turn up, he seemed to spend most of his time in good natured banter with younger colleagues. I began to fear that he was seriously exploring the idea of giving up experimental work altogether.

What tipped the balance the other way was Mei Lin. Let me explain that there was one aspect of Michael's personality that I didn't really fathom. He was, as you might expect, very attractive to women, but I could never quite make out whether they were attractive to him. They seemed to be encompassed in his general playfulness with people, and he was often seen about the town with strikingly glamorous creatures many years his junior. Sometimes it was the one glamorous creature for several months, but the attachment never seemed to become deep enough to form what is now known as a 'stable relationship' to say nothing of a marriage. Some of the gossips whispered that he was actually a homosexual who merely paraded women as a form of camouflage, but I found this very difficult to believe. I thought, on the contrary, that he had a deeply romantic, and perhaps still slightly adolescent, vision of what he was looking for in a woman, and that the modern world didn't any longer produce anything that came remotely near to meeting his specifications. So I saw his periodic liaisons not as hopeful forays into the unknown, and certainly not as camouflage, but rather as accommodations that he was driven to make from time to time *faute de mieux*. I thought nonetheless that he would one day settle for something like Celia Johnson in 'Brief Encounter' or

Greer Garson in 'Mrs Miniver', something very decent and very English. It was only after the event that I was able to see that his romantically exalted specifications could only have been met by the product of a totally different culture.

Mei Lin came to the department looking for work, any sort of work. She had been a lecturer in English at the University of Shanghai, but had fallen foul of the Communist authorities and had been dismissed from her post. During the cultural revolution both she and her husband had been incarcerated, but in different prisons. It was only after she was released that she learned that he had been executed. Unable to find any paid work, she had lived from hand to mouth for two or three years and then, somehow, had managed to escape to Hong Kong. By a route of infinite complexity, she finally reached this country and was granted political asylum. Her hope had been that she would be able to find some academic position here, but it soon became clear that this would be far from easy and, in the meantime, she had to eat. One of our Chinese graduate students had apparently encouraged her to try her luck with us, for there were indeed jobs to be done about the department that did not call for any scientific training.

Our administrator brought her to see me. She might have walked straight out of a scroll painting. She was wearing a severe dark grey tunic that buttoned up to the neck, and her face was a symmetrical oval from which the glossy black hair was pulled back into a ponytail. I thought her very beautiful, but what struck me most was the studied grace of her movements. When I asked her to sit down she put her feet and knees neatly together and folded her hands into her lap. She raised them only occasionally to make a controlled gesture as she spoke but they always returned to the same place. I took her on, of course, and had decided, even before our conversation was over, to put her in Michael's laboratory. His little group was rather short of technical assistance at the time, and I thought that Mei Lin could help with some of the time-consuming routine tasks. But there was an additional reason. Michael's inexhaustible intellectual curiosity had induced him to memorise a few thousand Chinese characters, and although I do not think that he spoke Chinese at all freely, he read it well enough to be able to make his way through some of the Chinese classics in the original. So there was every reason to hope that, with Michael, Mei Lin would not feel altogether lost. I had no doubt that he would find her at least interesting.

She began by doing some of the washing up and plugging the pipettes with cotton wool, but it wasn't long before she had assimilated some of the more complex operations going on in the laboratory and was making a much appreciated contribution to the work. But her effect on Michael was more immediate. He at once began to come into the laboratory every day and although, initially, it was merely to improve his Chinese, he must have decided that, as he was there in any case, he might as well do some work. There was, of course, no knowing what Michael would turn his attention to, but I wasn't too surprised to learn in due course that he had gone back to his old interest in receptors on cell surfaces. What worried him most about K.'s paper was the enormous disparity between the precision of the methods used and the magnitude of the claims made. Michael felt sure there was something of interest to be found in examining the hormone receptors of breast cancer cells, but he was also sure that much better methods would have to be developed for analysing these receptors before reproducible and interpretable results could be obtained.

He began by playing with the techniques everybody then used to study receptors of this kind, but after a few weeks he abandoned them altogether and struck out on a completely new tack. Michael in full flight was magnificent to behold. He was at the bench all day and, often enough, worked right through to the early hours of the morning. More than once when I had reason to return to the laboratory after an unusually tedious formal dinner, I saw the lights still on in his laboratory and, putting my head around the door, found him working away on some piece of apparatus with Mei Lin patient and helpful at his side. Before the year was out he was able to show me that K.'s great discovery was, without a doubt, an experimental artifact of a quite primitive kind. I, of course, urged him to publish at once, arguing that it was in the public interest to stop K. misleading people and misappropriating scarce research funds. But Michael wouldn't hear of it. "I don't care a hoot about K. and his shoddy experiments" he said, " I want to know what that wretched receptor really is doing. And I'm not going to publish anything until I have an answer that satisfies me." So he went on, month after month, hammering away at the problem, refining some of his techniques, abandoning others, and displaying in almost everything he did a level of ingenuity that none of us could match.

As time went by I got to know a little more about Mei Lin. It had puzzled me that someone brought up in Mao's China should have retained so aristocratic a manner, and the puzzlement was only partly dispelled when I learned that she was descended from a long line of distinguished forebears who had been scholar-administrators in the complex and subtle world of Imperial China. She could only have imbibed that style if her parents had been determined to impart it, and she would only have retained it in the face of the pressure exerted by the rigidly conformist communist state if she was convinced it was worth retaining. Her father had been a professor of Chinese Literature in the University of Shanghai and her mother had been one of his pupils. It appears that, for a while, her parents had been able to come to terms with the new political dispensation, at least outwardly, but in their home they clung to the traditions and cultural values of the society that had been swept away. It was in this secretive Marrano-like environment that Mei Lin had been moulded. When she herself entered the university she joined the communist youth movement with genuine enthusiasm, for she did not then see any incompatibility between the cultural traditions imparted by her parents and the demands made by the state. Indeed, she took the view, passionately held by many idealists at that time, in China and elsewhere, that natural justice required a fundamental restructuring of society. But eventually she was made all too aware of the corruption and the brutality of the regime under which she lived, and when the opportunity presented itself, she had come out openly for democracy. The price she paid was the loss of her parents, her husband, and her homeland.

It came as no surprise, of course, that the initially rather formal relations between Michael and Mei Lin soon gave way to something more intimate. I think the essential catalyst was the fact that both of them were natural aristocrats and each at once recognised this quality in the other. But they had much more than that in common: deeply held, and shared, convictions about how the world ought to be, great moral courage, and a complete disdain for the little vanities that lubricate the lives of lesser mortals. Despite the difference in age, they made a handsome couple, for Michael had never lost his boyishness and Mei Lin, for understandable reasons, was sage beyond her years. I began to think it possible that, this time, Michael might at last have found what he was looking for.

One day Michael came along with the draft of a paper that he wanted me to have a look at. It was only then that I grasped the magnitude of what he had done. The destruction of K.'s pretentious claims did not loom large in what he had written. In fact, the discussion of K.'s work was rather buried in the body of the text, as if his experiments simply weren't worth too much attention. This was not, I believe, a piece of affectation on Michael's part, but a genuine reflection of what he thought. What Michael had achieved was of a completely different order. He had first developed an effective method for purifying the hormone receptor and had then studied its structure in minute detail. The information so gained enabled him, by a difficult and circuitous route, to isolate the gene that specified the receptor, and he then went on to analyse the structure of the gene. What he found out was that the breast cancer cells had the same hormone receptor as normal breast cells (not an additional receptor, as K. had claimed), but, in the cancer cells, the gene was damaged in such a way that an abnormal receptor was produced. The behaviour of this abnormal receptor was dramatically interesting: it permitted the cancer cells to go on multiplying under conditions where normal cells couldn't. I don't need to tell you how important all this was, but perhaps I should say that it was the first time that a gene for a hormone receptor had been isolated, and the astonishing behaviour of the altered receptor at once provided a plausible explanation for the fact that breast cancers that initially respond to hormone treatment may later become resistant to it.

Michael, who had nothing but contempt for self-advertisement, wouldn't consider publishing the work in one of the noisy magazines like *Nature*, but submitted it, as he did with all his papers, to an upright and conservative journal whose profits were ploughed back into scientific research. Nonetheless, when his paper appeared, it caught the attention of one of the editors of *Nature* who, in a very laudatory commentary, described the work as both a 'breakthrough' and a 'milestone'. Perhaps because anything that brings together the words 'breakthrough' and 'cancer' makes good copy for newspapers, the commentary in *Nature* was picked up by the national press, and Michael, much to his annoyance, found himself at the centre of public attention. One consequence of this, however, was that, a few months later, Michael received a most unusual letter from the chairman of the research organisation that had previously funded his work. It contained an expression of regret that an ill-advised decision had been taken to terminate this funding and an offer not only to reinstate it but to expand it in any way that Michael thought would be helpful.

But much the best thing that happened to Michael in that wonderful year was that Mei Lin agreed to marry him. The wedding took place in a picturesque Elizabethan schoolroom that served as a registry office in one of our neighbouring towns. There was nobody from Mei Lin's family at the simple ceremony, so I felt a little as if I was the one who was giving her away. Their first child, a girl, was born about a year later and the second, a boy, about a year after that. As I watched the two toddlers grow, I couldn't help noting how beautiful the children of such mixed marriages often turn out to be.

You might think that K. would have been chastened by such a humiliating exposure of his scientific incompetence. Nothing of the sort. He continued to prate away on television, and I once actually heard him say that it was the work in his laboratory that had drawn attention to the importance of the hormone receptor in breast cancer and had led to the interesting experiments that Michael had done. Well, as Abraham Lincoln is reputed to have said, you can fool all of the people some of the time and some of the people all of the time, but you cannot fool all the people all the time. Despite his plausibility and his diligence, K. soon found, to his dismay, that he was being quietly dropped from the committees that were his natural habitat; and within a couple of years the only people who asked for his opinion were the television interviewers. The last time I heard him talk was at a meeting in London where he delivered his usual polished, but vacuous, lecture. I happened to be sitting next to an eminent surgeon who had formerly been one of his staunchest supporters. As K. stepped down from the rostrum, my neighbour leaned over to me and whispered: "I think old K. is past his prime. Does he imagine he can go on hoodwinking us for ever? I hear he has a cottage in the south of France. He would make an important contribution to science in this country if he spent more time there." I agreed, of course, but I doubted that such high grace would befall us.

CHAPTER 8

SEXUAL HARASSMENT

In the tidal wave of paper that washes across my desk each day, there arrived one morning a document concerning sexual harassment. It coincided with the riveting spectacle of Anita Hill testifying to the Senate of the United States that Clarence Thomas had many years previously subjected her to sexual harassment and was therefore not a fit person to serve as a judge of the United States Supreme Court. Not unexpectedly, the accusation was denied by Clarence Thomas, and it soon became apparent that his appointment to this distinguished office hinged on whether the members of the Senate believed him or her. As is now well known, the vote, by a narrow margin, went his way, but anyone who took an interest in the proceedings would have seen that neither side was able to produce one shred of tangible evidence. What determined the vote was a mixture of subjective personal impressions and political considerations that had nothing to do with the veracity of the two adversaries. They were both polished performers, and it is difficult to see how, in such circumstances, a decision based on rational criteria could ever be reached. This is not, of course, an uncommon situation in legal proceedings, but it seems to me that, in the absence of witnesses, evidence or observable consequences, the charge of sexual harassment is peculiarly difficult either to substantiate or to refute.

The document that reached my desk contained some legalistic definitions, an elaborate set of procedures that we were asked to follow if an accusation of sexual harassment was made within the sphere of our responsibility, and an outline of the judicial process that could, if necessary, be brought into play. Public pressure now demands that university legislation should include provisions for dealing with sexual harassment, and perhaps (though I doubt it) such provisions might act as a deterrent; but I could not help wondering, as I ploughed my way through the densely typed paper, whether we would be any more skilful in arriving at the truth than the Senate of the United States. My ambivalence was not, however, determined solely by the televised confrontation between Anita Hill and Clarence Thomas. What kept running through my mind was an episode that took place long before sexual harassment had become a focus of public attention, indeed long before the term was used at all.

No man who has taught undergraduates for any length of time can have failed to come across the pretty girl who sits in the front row and makes eyes at you all the way through your lecture. A stock figure in modern American fiction and, it seems, a genuine hazard in some places. I have been lecturing to undergraduates for well nigh thirty years and, in a vague sort of way, can recall a whole string of these entertaining creatures. I am grateful to them too, for enlivening the tedium of grinding through the same old stuff yet one more time. But Angela V. is graven in my memory with unusual precision. She sailed into my first lecture of the year a few minutes late, and mine was not the only pair of eyes that turned to gawk at her. It was at the time that miniskirts, under the influence of Jean Shrimpton, were just beginning to make their way hesitantly into what might be called respectable dress, and the simple bright red thing that Angela had on had a hemline that went as high as decency then permitted. She would have been striking even in the most sober attire. Taller than average, and fashionably slender, with long blond hair that fell loosely about her shoulders, she looked as if her natural habitat was the world of *haute couture*. I would have regarded her face as complacently pretty, but uninteresting, had it not been for her large grey eyes in which, to my surprise, I failed to find any hint of invitation or even a flicker of amusement. In fact, as they gazed up at me, what I thought I saw in them was something not too far from despair.

On that first day she squeezed into one end of the front row, but after that she must have come early, for she was always there in the centre of the row directly opposite me. She obviously had a large amount of money to spend on clothes, for there was something different, but always provocative, each week, and I didn't see the little red mini again until the end of the term. When she took notes she seemed to labour over the writing, like a child, and then she would look up with those extraordinary eyes, appealing to me for God knows what – nothing, in any case, that I was in a position to give her. It didn't surprise me at all to learn that she had been the object of unwanted sexual advances. What I found puzzling was that she had found it necessary to lodge a formal complaint about it; and I was absolutely astonished when I heard that the man she had named was Adrian F.

I had known Adrian for many years. He was a popular and highly successful medical tutor whose pupils were regularly to be found high in the class lists of the final examinations. He had long held a tutorial fellowship at one of the largest and most affluent of the colleges, and this, together with his reputation as a teacher, had enabled him to attract a string of talented undergraduates. His research was in what might strike an outsider as a rather obscure area of physiology, but his influence over his pupils was such that many of them chose, after graduation, to join his laboratory, so that he managed, despite heavy college commitments, to sustain a continuously high output of experimental work. All this was admirable enough, but it was only a minor component of the glamour that surrounded him; for he was an eminently eligible bachelor with romantic good looks that to me suggested a mature reincarnation of Rupert Brooke, and he was very rich. Very rich men were by then already something of a rarity in academic life, and although he was much too subtle to indulge in any conscious display of wealth, it couldn't escape our notice that he drove an expensive handmade car (a Lagonda, I think it was), that he had a London address in the best part of Holland Park, and that during the summer vacation he went off to something like a small chateau in the Vaucluse which seemed to be his own. What's more, he continued to entertain undergraduates and colleagues in the high style that had been all but killed off by the war. His dinners were always memorable, not because of exotic foods and rare vintages (I once heard him say that rare vintages were for rare occasions), but because he took as much care in selecting his guests as he did in deciding every detail of the menu. I knew next to nothing about his private life, but had I been asked, I would have guessed that he was irresistibly attractive to young women and that he no doubt had great difficulty in evading their eager attentions. I therefore found it very difficult to believe that he would have been overwhelmed by Angela's flamboyant display of her charms, considerable though they were; and it was inconceivable to me that this urbane and sensitive man would have behaved with the adolescent crudity that Angela accused him of.

University and college authorities worry much less about what actually goes on in such cases than they do about the public scandal that ensues if the news leaks out. They therefore make every effort to resolve the complaint informally and do their best to hush things up. It was Angela's insistence on a formal enquiry that made secrecy impossible in her case. Long before the proceedings started, the tabloid newspapers, with their customary self-righteousness, were wallowing in stories about a distinguished scientist who was accused by a pretty young undergraduate (see photo) of making unwanted sexual advances during tutorials and of threatening her with failure in the examinations unless she agreed to have intercourse with him. Now whatever one might have thought of the plausibility of Adrian making unwanted sexual advances to Angela during tutorials, the idea that he would have threatened her with failure in the examinations was preposterous. This university is so obsessed with the results of the final examinations that infinite pains are taken to ensure that the marking of the papers is as fair as it can be. Several examiners are involved in assessing each paper and any anomalous mark is closely scrutinised. So if the story wasn't invented by an excited journalist writing under the influence of an American novel, then Angela was not only malevolent, she was also remarkably ignorant of university practice. My own view was that Adrian would never have made so empty a threat and Angela would never have taken it seriously even if it had been made.

When I was asked to join the small panel of university elders that was set up to look into the matter, my initial reaction was that I ought to decline. I had already come to the conclusion that Adrian was innocent of the charge brought against him, and that was not an appropriate frame of mind for someone who was expected to exercise an impartial judicial function. But then it seemed to me that none of the other members of the makeshift court was likely to be any more impartial than I was, and perhaps our differing prejudices would cancel each other out. So, in the end, I agreed to join, but continued to view the whole procedure with great unease.

I expected that Angela would present herself in the most demure possible light, but when she entered the room it was clear that I had underestimated her. She had chosen for the occasion a deep blue mini that set off her blond hair and grey eyes to perfection, and the old men looking at her as she sat down to face them reminded me of Susanna and the Elders. It was obviously her intention to convince us that even the most staid and respectable of men might lose his head if the temptation was strong enough; and as I glanced at my colleagues I had no doubt that she had succeeded in making her point.

Her story was that Adrian had begun by putting his arm around her shoulders or patting her on the thigh when he was pleased with some observation she had made. But this apparently affectionate behaviour was soon accompanied by remarks or jokes with ambiguous overtones, and these, she claimed, had eventually given way to overtly sexual advances which were reinforced by threats of failure in the final examinations. A perfectly commonplace story, but one that I had the greatest difficulty in reconciling with the Adrian F. I knew. Why should Adrian who, I imagined, could have any girl he wanted, suddenly become recklessly infatuated with this particular one whose style was so unsubtle? And the picture of Adrian pawing the girl against her wishes and threatening to fail her in the examinations was one that I simply couldn't envisage. However, when it was Adrian's turn to state his case, he did it very ineptly. He began by asserting that he did not find the girl at all sexually attractive. There was no need for him to say this and, naturally, none of us believed him. It was possible, he admitted, that he might have put his arm around her shoulder or patted her, but he couldn't remember having done so and, if he had, he insisted that it was done in all innocence. He denied that he had ever made any sexual advances to her and claimed, on the contrary, that it was she who had made advances to him and that he had rebuffed them. He poured scorn on the accusation that he had threatened her with failure in the examinations, but he did not answer it.

Well, as always, it boiled down to whether we believed her or him. We accepted that it was unlikely that he had attempted to blackmail her with the threats she described. But we thought, on balance, that he probably had laid hands on her in a manner that, at the very least, could easily have been misinterpreted; and we took the view that in a sensitive situation of this kind, we could expect an experienced teacher to behave with the utmost circumspection. We did not explore the claim that it was she who had made the sexual advances for, as we saw it, she would not have made such advances unless there was something about his behaviour that suggested that they would not be rebuffed. We concluded that Adrian's misdemeanour was not serious enough to warrant the instigation of formal disciplinary procedures, but we thought it appropriate to reprimand him for behaviour that fell short of the highest standards and, in particular, for permitting himself a degree of familiarity with his pupil that was, in the circumstances, inevitably prone to mis-interpretation. It was our hope that a semi-official reprimand of this kind would satisfy Angela and that she would not then feel it necessary to take the matter any further. And that is exactly what happened. The newspapers huffed and puffed about a cover-up and put out imaginative tales of Adrian's academic colleagues secretly closing ranks; but Angela seemed suddenly to have lost all interest in the proceedings, and although tongues continued to wag in the common rooms for a week or two, the whole business rapidly became yesterday's news. Except for Adrian.

The difficulty with allegations of sexual harassment is that they tarnish irreparably, even when they eventually turn out to be groundless. Adrian endeavoured to resume his normal life in college and in the laboratory, but the accusations that Angela had made clung to him like a shadow. For two years running, there was a precipitous fall in the number and quality of the applications that his college received from prospective undergraduates who wanted to study medicine, and none of his pupils chose to join his laboratory on graduation. I think he was convinced that wherever he went the whiff of sexual misconduct went with him, even when he was with old friends who believed him to be totally innocent of any conscious wrongdoing. On two occasions I was on the verge of explaining my own position but couldn't quite do it, partly because I was far from proud of having concurred in the reprimand that he had been given, and partly because it seemed so pointless once the milk had been spilt. In the end he gave up and, having the means to do so, not only resigned from his post but left the country altogether. I did not see him again for several years, but heard that he was living the life of a country gentleman in the Vaucluse. As for Angela, we never did find out what she was capable of in the examinations, for she abandoned her studies a few months after the enquiry had ended, and no-one seemed to know what she did next.

I did, however, learn a little more about her, but too late, regrettably, to influence the course of events. It was the merest chance that Angela's path and Adrian's had crossed at all. There were no coeducational colleges in the university at the time, and it was only because the medical tutor at Angela's college was on sabbatical leave that an arrangement had been made for her to have some tutorials from Adrian. I don't often get invitations to dine at the women's colleges, but shortly after the gossip about Adrian and Angela had died down, I received such an invitation from the senior tutor at her college. As I hardly knew the lady, I naturally assumed that the invitation had some specific purpose, and I was not mistaken. It was Angela that she proposed to talk about. Needless to say, the last thing I wanted, as a member of the panel that had reprimanded Adrian, was a postmortem on the affair. But the senior tutor was a formidable woman and she was not to be deterred.

"I think you have quite the wrong impression of Angela V." she began. "Perhaps so," I said "but could you tell me, please, why she dresses as she does and flaunts herself at every possible opportunity if she doesn't want to provoke sexual advances?" "Of course she wants to provoke sexual advances," came the reply "but only in order to repel them. Almost every man who comes within her orbit makes a pass at her, but none of them ever gets anywhere." And she went on to paint a picture that was indeed very different from what I had imagined.

It transpired that Angela was the child of a broken home, and her father, immensely wealthy, was a celebrated philanderer whose escapades were often featured in the Sunday pictorials. Her relations with her mother were icy, and she had spent most of her life in expensive boarding schools where, naturally enough, she had been very unhappy and later became rebellious. For reasons that were not made clear to me, a school friend of hers who was also a member of the college had provided some information about the form which that rebellion took. In fashionable girls' schools at that time, sex was a subterranean subject, but Angela had apparently made it the centre of her daily life. She talked about little else, regaled her classmates with tales of torrid affairs she claimed to have had in the vacations, and entertained them with imitations of bump and grind routines that she had seen in the cinema. She was, nonetheless, a very good student and, having narrowly escaped expulsion, gained a place in the college of her choice with the minimum of effort. Nobody had any idea why she chose medicine, for she didn't seem much interested in any part of it. Her undergraduate career had so far been little more than an elaborate extension of her schoolgirl rebellion, but the senior tutor was convinced that it was all display. "I don't believe she has ever been to bed with a man," she concluded, "and I have little doubt that something much more serious than a sexual advance must have taken place between her and Adrian F. Why should she make a public issue of yet one more sexual advance?" I heard her out and thanked her for the information, but I couldn't resist adding that it would have been much more helpful if it had been offered before, rather than after, the enquiry.

When I had had time to digest what I had been told I constructed a Freudian fable of my own. I agreed that the crucial question was indeed Angela's motivation. Why had she insisted on a process that would inevitably inflict public humiliation on Adrian whether he was found guilty or not? I ruled out the possibility that something more serious than a sexual advance had been committed. No-one who knew Adrian at all well could entertain that notion, and it made no sense for Angela to have accused him of a lesser offence if he had committed a greater one. It seemed to me that Angela would only have wanted to humiliate him if he had humiliated her. Now Adrian was not one of those barbarous tutors who take pleasure in belittling the intellectual efforts of their pupils. On the contrary, it was well known that he was kindly and even generous in that

113

respect. In any case, that form of humiliation was too petty to have engendered so dramatic a response. The only possibility that I could see was that Adrian was telling the truth when he claimed that it was she who had made the sexual advances and he who had rejected them. In the light of what I had heard from the senior tutor at her college, an initiative of this kind from Angela would have been wholly out of character: she did not make sexual advances, she provoked them. But what if her feelings for Adrian had actually been deeper than anyone had imagined? What if, for the first time in her life, she had actually fallen in love? She would not have been the first undergraduate to be swept off her feet by this handsome and accomplished man. Would not his maturity, his gentleness, the well ordered stability of his life have been exactly what she was looking for? And what greater humiliation could there be for someone like Angela, the lodestone of masculine attention, than to be rejected by the one man to whom she had ever offered herself? All this, although perhaps a little pat, was plausible enough, but it left one crucial question unanswered. Why did Adrian, a bachelor with no other ties as far as we knew and with apparently nothing to lose, reject her? It was a long time before I had the answer to that question.

When Adrian had said at the enquiry that he was not sexually attracted to Angela, no member of the panel took the denial seriously. We all knew Adrian as a man whom most women found fascinating and who evidently enjoyed female company – the sophisticated bachelor who had not yet been caught. We had no reason to suspect that the overt picture with which we were familiar might have been deeply different from the reality. I don't believe it occurred to any one of us that Adrian might have found Angela sexually unattractive simply because she was a woman. Our innocence perhaps requires an explanation. At that time, the battle for emancipation of homosexuals had indeed begun, but social attitudes still lagged far behind the legal reforms that had been enacted. The great majority of homosexuals still took immense pains to disguise their sexual orientation; and those who themselves had no homosexual inclinations rarely knew much about the subject or were at all interested to find out. I think most people still carried in their heads the effeminate stereotype of the music halls, and if there was no visible element in a man's behaviour that conformed to that stereotype, the suspicion that he might be homosexual would not have arisen, even if other circumstances had suggested it. Be that as it may, the idea that Adrian was homosexual, and exclusively so, did not enter my mind until it was forcefully put there by a conversation I had some years after the event with a young historian at Adrian's former college. We were sitting together at dinner and exchanging unenterprising comments about this and that, when, quite abruptly, as if he had finally made up his mind to get something off his chest, the smile left his face and he said to me: "You should know that you did Adrian F. a great injustice. There is no possibility whatever that he made any sexual advances to Angela V". And then, hesitantly, almost as if he were making a confession, he added: "And I am in a position to know."

I had been reluctant to take part in the judicial process, uneasy about associating myself with its conclusions, increasingly concerned, as time went by, at what we had done; but after that conversation I felt that I could no longer let the matter rest. I managed to get Adrian's address in France from one of his old friends and wrote to ask whether he would agree to see me when next I happened to be in that part of the world. A couple of weeks later I received a courteous reply in which he not only said that he would be very pleased to see me again, but also offered to put me up for a day or two if that fitted in with my plans.

Before the academic world closed down for the summer, I had engineered an invitation to lecture in Marseilles. I flew down at the end of September and, after I had done my duty, hired a car to drive at my leisure to Fontaine-de-Vaucluse, where I made my obeisance to Petrarch, and then on to the hill village where Adrian lived. The small white houses clustered around a much larger structure which I would not have called a chateau although some bits of it might have been a fortress in the days of the Saracens. It was behind those forbidding walls that Adrian had made his home. To my surprise, he greeted me with what appeared to be genuine warmth and, apart from the grey at his temples, I found him little changed. When I had settled in, he showed me round the medieval rooms that he had restored and furnished as only a rich man can – fortunately, in this case, a rich man with taste. He took obvious pleasure in what he had achieved. Then we went off for a stroll through the village and watched the hills turn violet as the sun went down.

He had not, I was glad to hear, entirely abandoned physiology. Although he was no longer able to do any experimental work, he continued to subscribe to three or four of the main physiological journals and occasionally attended seminars in Marseilles or Montpellier where he had some contacts. He had apparently developed a serious interest in the history of the famous old medical school at Montpellier and especially in Raymond Vieussens, whose work on heart disease he proposed eventually to make the subject of a monograph. He still had his flat in Holland Park, but had bought another in Paris, in the seizième arrondissement, and spent more time there than in London.

We dined alone in one of the less grand rooms in his house: avocado mousse and quail prepared and served by an elderly lady whose manner reminded me of Proust's Francioise. I was curious to know whether he had succeeded in penetrating the indigenous village community which, I imagined, would be hermetically sealed against outsiders; and I was given an unexpected insight into rural French chauvinism. "These people" he said, "are not any more xenophobic than anyone else, but they are desperately anxious to preserve their cultural traditions. It is difficult for someone who lives in an English-speaking country to sense how gravely threatened these traditions now are. But rural France is not inhospitable. If you take the trouble to speak French, no matter how inept your French is, and if you seek the friendship of those about you, you will find yourself drawn into their daily life much more easily , I expect, than you would in a remote English village. I have two or three people over to dinner at least once a month, and I am always asked back." It sounded a good enough recipe, but the essential ingredient, it seemed to me, was Adrian's intrinsic likeability. I looked at him as he spoke and couldn't help thinking that this was a man who would find acceptance in any civilized society.

When, finally, the plates were cleared and a splendidly misshapen bottle of old Armagnac found its way to our table, I decided that the moment had come for me to declare the purpose of my visit. I began by asking whether he knew what had brought me to seek him out. "Of course" he replied. I confessed then that I had long been tormented by what we had done and had decided, if there was no way in which the injustice could be remedied, that I must at least make an abject apology. "There's no need for that" he said, "and no need for the remorse either. I knew that you didn't believe what that wretched girl was saying and that you agreed to go along with the majority view only because you thought it would be the least damaging thing to do. And what else could you have done anyway? Do you think I would have thanked you then, if you had persuaded the panel that the accusation was false on the ground that I was a man who did not love women?" I felt I had to ask him whether there was any point in my reopening the case now. "Quite pointless." he answered "I shall never go back. The French have always been more understanding in these matters than the English and they still are." I drove back to Marseilles the following day, and although I sometimes pick up a scrap of news about Adrian from one or other of his former colleagues, I have not seen him since.

But I did see Angela again – just once. There was this period of total eclipse for a year or two after she fled from our university, and then photographs of her began to appear in the gossip pages of newspapers and in the sort of magazine that you read in your dentist's waiting room. That's how I came to notice her in an issue of *Vogue*. She was clinging affectionately to the arm of an elegant white-haired man who, it appeared, was a well known art-dealer. A couple of years after that, there was a piece about her and her husband in the colour supplement of the Sunday paper that I buy now and again when I'm feeling idle. Her husband was not the art-dealer I'd seen in *Vogue*, but a banker. From what was said about him, you would have concluded that he was a paragon of civic virtue, and I guessed he must have been at least twenty years her senior.

Now I am the last person you might expect to meet in the company of those who fill the pages of *Vogue*; but, a few months after the article about Angela and her husband appeared in my Sunday paper, I received an invitation to a gala evening arranged by one of the cancer charities and, of course, I felt duty-bound to go. I was trying hard to make conversation with a very rich man who wanted to know why we scientists hadn't yet found a cure for cancer, when, out of the corner of my eye, I saw Angela and her husband enter the room. She was still strikingly beautiful, but her beauty was now honed and polished, and there wasn't one blond hair out of place. As she moved towards us, I caught her attention and was about to speak to her, for I was sure that she had recognized me, but she sailed straight past and made for a far corner where she had no difficulty in avoiding me for the rest of the evening. After that, as far as I can remember, no further images of Angela's social progress came to my notice. Then, one day, flipping through the staid pages of our university gazette, I saw her name among the obituaries. They gave her maiden name in brackets, so I couldn't be mistaken, but the married name she bore at the time of her death was certainly not that of the banker I had seen her with.

I do not know many psychiatrists, but one of my undergraduate cronies, David W., ended up as a superintendent of a large private psychiatric institution on the outskirts of London. Many of these places are more concerned with money than they are with mental health, but David was an honourable man and the establishment he ran was efficient and kindly. For old times' sake, we exchange visits every couple of years, and it so happened that I'd arranged to visit him soon after my return from the Vaucluse. Now David is not the sort of doctor who talks about his patients, but when I mentioned that I had seen Adrian, whom he had known quite well, he couldn't resist telling me that Angela had been his patient. "It was the saddest of lives," he said, "repeated bouts of deep depression and, towards the end, unremitting insomnia. You do know, don't you, that she went through three marriages, but as far as I could see, she didn't derive much pleasure from any of them." "How did she die?" I asked. He seemed reluctant to give me an answer, but, after a long pause and shaking his head slowly, he relented: "Like a film star unable to face the prospect of her summer coming to an end. There was a bottle of pills, all but empty, on the table beside her bed." I still see David from time to time, but it seems that neither of us much wants to talk about Angela.

This morning, a revised version of the rules for dealing with sexual harassment reached my desk. The new rules are all-inclusive: they deal in one and the same breath with sexual harassment, harassment on grounds of religion or colour, harassment of one undergraduate by another. It seems to me that there are distinctions to be made. I don't suppose that I shall be asked now to serve on another judicial panel, but if I am and it's a case of sexual harassment, I don't think I could bring myself to do it.

CHAPTER 9

DIWALI IN AGRA

I first saw the Taj Mahal through a veil of gentle rain. As you enter the walled garden through the main gate you do not see the red sandstone base on which the white marble rests. That's why the guide books all talk of the tomb floating over the Yamuna river like a mirage. When the early morning light is broken by rain, the outlines of the dome and the minarets are further softened, and the sense of illusion is then inescapable. Photographs of the Taj make it look like a white building, and so it is from afar, but as you come nearer, you see that the white is suffused with colour which increases in intensity as the brilliant decoration comes into focus. Within the tomb itself, the walls are a riot of bright semi-precious stones set into the marble in exuberant floral patterns. I had not, however, come to Agra to admire the Taj Mahal (although there is no monument that I admire more) and certainly not to write about it. I had come to visit the small group of nondescript buildings that sit right beside it. I wonder how many of the millions of tourists who walk down the tree-lined paths to the mausoleum have ever glanced at its unprepossessing neighbour and wondered what it was for. Well, it's a research institute and a small hospital for the study and treatment of leprosy; and it struck me when I first saw where it was located that the juxtaposition of the Taj and a leprosy hospital was, in a way, a symbol of the two faces of India.

I was on a lecture tour that was to take me to several of the main centres of medical research in India, and although the institute beside the Taj did not fall into that category, the subtle scholar who was my host and who had arranged my itinerary had evidently

120

thought that a trip to Agra might make a deeper contribution to my education than I suspected. He was right. In rural India, leprosy is more than a disease; it is a social and moral catastrophe. The leper is an outcast not only because his presence defiles those who come into contact with him, but also because, for true believers, leprosy is unequivocal evidence of divine retribution for past depravity, either in this life or a previous one. In the ambience of a Hindu village, an individual who contracts leprosy does not seek medical attention, but, on the contrary, does his best to conceal his condition for as long as possible; and when, as inevitably happens, the secret is discovered, the leper has no choice but to abandon hearth and home and take to the road. His fate thereafter is uncertain but more often than not disastrous. In the wards of the hospital, I therefore saw not only the early stages of the disease, which nowadays are usually amenable to treatment, but also disfigured faces and severe deformities of hands and feet to which inventive surgeons endeavoured to restore a modicum of function. Some of the staff were themselves cured lepers, and it was difficult to escape the impression that the whole establishment was carried on a wave of selfless dedication.

As the research institute associated with the hospital was not a large operation, I managed to spend a little time with each of the scientists working there. That's how I came to have my first conversation with Hari. The director of the institute had already spoken to me about him. There had apparently been leprosy in his family, and Hari had been fatherless from an early age. How he came to complete a scientific education was something of a miracle, but as soon as he was able to understand what was involved, he had decided to devote his life to the study of leprosy. The director considered him the most gifted of the young men who had passed through his hands. He was very small, with unusually dark skin, from which I inferred a South Indian origin, and his rather angelic face reminded me of photographs I had seen of the young Krishnamurti. Beneath a clean white laboratory coat he wore Indian clothes – a kurta and loose trousers – and I sensed at a glance that in this man the East and the West were at war.

Because leprosy was such an immense medical and social problem in India, it was not surprising that several laboratories in different parts of the country had embarked on programmes aimed at developing vaccines against the disease. I asked Hari what he thought the chances were that one or other of these efforts would lead to an effective vaccine. He was at first reluctant to give an opinion and looked at me rather suspiciously, as if he were concerned that if he told me what he really thought, I might pass his views on to higher authority. But I managed to reassure him that I was genuinely interested in what he had to say, and that our conversation would, of course, be confidential. Then, hesitantly at first, he opened up, and I was given the best half-hour's tutorial on leprosy that I had ever had. It transpired that he didn't hold out much hope for an effective vaccine, at least not for the conventional vaccines that were being developed.

"You see," he said, "although the clinical picture can be very different, the basic biology of leprosy is not unlike that of tuberculosis, and despite the best efforts of many people over more than half a century no really useful vaccine was ever produced for tuberculosis." In his view, what we needed was a much deeper understanding of the elements that govern the growth of the leprosy bacillus in the cells that it parasitizes, and, with immense enthusiasm, he explained how he had set about exploring this question. It was not an easy task. At that time it was almost impossible to grow the leprosy bacillus except in armadillos, and he had managed to collect a few of these animals in order to produce enough material to work with. Then he had introduced the bacilli into cells taken from individuals who had succumbed to leprosy, and cells from others who, though constantly exposed to the disease, had failed to contract it. He had studied the fate of the bacilli in the two situations and thought that he could detect interesting differences. It would have been a creditable performance anywhere, but with the limited facilities available to him in Agra, it was splendid. That evening at dinner, the director asked me what I thought of Hari, to which I replied that he obviously had the makings of a first class scientist and seemed, in other respects, to be a wholly admirable man. "Do you think", he went on to ask, "that there is any chance that you might be able to take him into your laboratory for a year or two to broaden his range and expose him to some of the more complex techniques that are not easily available to him here in India?" I promised that when I got back I would see what I could do.

In those days, grant-giving bodies were not hamstrung by tiers of committees or strategic plans or the profitless philosophy of peer review. A single letter to London got Hari his travelling expenses and a modest, but not derisory, stipend for two years. He arrived, shivering, in the middle of a more than usually gloomy English winter. When he knocked on my door he was still wearing his Indian clothes, inadequately shielded from an east wind by a threadbare overcoat. I sent him off to get some warm clothes and told him that his first piece of research in his new environment would be to find somewhere to live. That's exactly what my supervisor had said to me when I arrived on his doorstep a couple of decades earlier. The colleges had not yet begun to take an interest in graduate students, to say nothing of postdoctoral fellows, and the best that could be hoped for was that one of the affluent colleges might offer Hari an occasional meal. In all other respects he would have to fend for himself. It took an inordinately long time for the university and its colleges to accept that they owed stray waifs from overseas at least a modicum of hospitality.

A few days later, Hari turned up in blue jeans and a huge grey pullover that displayed a team of reindeer galloping across his chest. He had taken his first step on the road to assimilation. It had apparently not been easy for him to find accommodation that he could afford, for he had to have at least a gas ring on which to cook his own meals, and most landladies didn't like the thought of that. Hari explained to me that he was a vegetarian, not exactly on religious grounds but because he simply couldn't reconcile himself to the idea of eating animal flesh, and he thought that he would find it difficult to adjust straight away to the English version of a vegetarian diet. He had finally managed to find a room in a rather dilapidated Victorian house that was largely occupied by Caribbean immigrants with whom he did not seem to be altogether at ease.

I decided to take Hari into my own laboratory. He had at first been eager to continue his work on the growth of leprosy bacilli, but I managed to persuade him that that wasn't a sensible thing to do. He hadn't, after all, come to us in order to do exactly what he had been doing in Agra. Would it not be more profitable for him in the

123

long run to take on board the newer approaches that we had to offer and apply them to the study of leprosy when he returned to India? He was, understandably, very reluctant to be deflected from what he had decided to make his life's work, but in the end I won him round. I was at the time attempting to develop a satisfactory procedure for measuring oxygen concentrations in very small volumes of fluid in order to see what effect restriction of oxygen supply would have on certain of the cells I was interested in. It seemed to me that one of the factors that Hari had not taken into account in his own experiments was the possibility that the results he had obtained might have been influenced by unmeasured variations in oxygen concentration. I had no doubt that if he spent a couple of years working with me on the problem of oxygen measurement, what he would learn would notably enhance the precision of any experiments that he later undertook with leprosy bacilli. But that wasn't the only reason I had for bringing him within my own immediate orbit. I guessed that for Hari, who had never been out of India and who felt ill at ease even in Delhi, the cultural transition to our way of life might require a little assistance.

He had not been in the laboratory for long before I realised that although he knew a great deal about leprosy there were some pretty sizeable gaps in his general biological, and especially biochemical, background. At first he attempted to disguise this, pretending to knowledge that he didn't have, but when I made it plain that I didn't care a hoot about what he knew or didn't know, but cared a great deal about how he set about repairing any defects there might be in his knowledge, he stopped the silly pretence and quickly demonstrated that if there was something of importance to his work that he didn't know, that state of ignorance did not last long. In fact, his capacity to assimilate new information and retain it accurately was astounding. But as our work together got under way, I noticed something else that disturbed me a great deal more than the gaps in his knowledge. He had an almost telepathic ability to divine how I expected an experiment to turn out, and he felt that it was incumbent on him to do his best to make it turn out that way, or at least to give the results an interpretation that was compatible with what he thought was in my mind. And if the results were hopelessly incompatible with this, he would say that the experiment had failed for technical reasons rather than tell me directly that my idea was wrong. I did not find it easy to make him realise that this course of action was perilous for us both. But the penny finally dropped, and then he went to great lengths to prove me wrong, which was an improvement but still far from ideal. Some months went by before he was prepared to let the experiments speak for themselves.

When you work closely with a young colleague and have a hand in shaping his scientific style, an element of paternalism inevitably creeps into the relationship. As time goes by, you begin to talk about things other than science and sometimes, if there is a meeting of minds, the conversation may drift into subjects that people are often reluctant to discuss. On Hari's desk, there was a small stone carving of Ganesha, the elephant-headed son of Shiva and Parvati, a god who removed obstacles, but also a divine patron of literature and learning. I asked Hari one day whether he kept it there as an ornament or a mascot or whether, perhaps, he viewed it much as a Christian would view a small crucifix. He was not at all eager to discuss the Ganesha and, for a moment, I rather regretted having asked the question. But then he decided that my curiosity was innocent and he gave me, not an answer, but an explanation.

"An educated Hindu is not nowadays an idolator" he said. "We see the gods in our pantheon as symbolic representations of the forces that govern the world – traditional metaphors if you like." "And do educated Hindus pray to these metaphors?" I asked. "Do they believe in the efficacy of prayer?" "It would be foolish to indulge in generalisations" he replied. "Many do not, even when, for social or other reasons, they adhere to certain rituals. But some continue to believe that there is still room in our universe for mystery, and then their attitude to prayer is little different from that of believers anywhere else." "And what about belief in an afterlife?" I went on. "Ah," he said "in India that has a quite special significance. For all but a tiny handful of us, life is very harsh. How can you tell a simple man whose life, through no fault of his own, is unrelievably miserable, that that's the luck of the draw and that's all there is? To preserve his sanity, he is bound to hope that he has another chance. And if he is to sustain some sense of justice, how can he escape the belief that his present wretchedness, unwarranted by anything he has done in this life, is a punishment for sins committed in another? One of the difficulties that Hindus have with Christianity is that there are only two lives, this and the next. Why only two? If there is no life before this one, what possible moral justification can you provide for gratuitous suffering – the slow painful death of a child from some inherited disease, for example? It is no help to say that the ways of God are mysterious. That is not an explanation that any Hindu could find convincing."

Carried away by his argument, Hari had gone further than he intended, and he broke off in some embarrassment. I hastened to assure him that I greatly appreciated his having explained these matters to me, but, to tell the truth, I was dissatisfied with what he had said, for although he had given me a lucid, if rather conventional, account of the views that an educated Hindu might hold, he had not divulged what his own position was and, in particular, he had scrupulously avoided any mention of the struggle between western science and Hindu spirituality that was determining the future course of his life.

A few weeks after his arrival, I took Hari in to dinner at my college. I had told him that I would order a vegetarian meal and he responded by turning up in his Indian attire. He had the usual preconceptions about what went on at high table and was not therefore surprised at all the rituals. In fact, he seemed to enjoy them. But he was rather disconcerted by the amount of elaborate food that was dispensed and asked me what was done with the large residues that many people left on the dishes. I told him that some of the uneaten food might well be re-used in some way but that most of it would in all probability be thrown away. That brought a frown to his face. "No Brahmin" he explained "would touch food that had been partially eaten by someone else". And then, almost as an afterthought: "Would it not be better to serve less than to throw food away when so much of the world goes hungry?" I did not attempt to justify our profligacy but did venture the observation that conspicuous waste seemed to be a concomitant of affluence even in the poorest countries.

Fortunately Hari's other neighbour at table was that most erudite of art historians, Simon T. who, among many other things, knew a great deal about South Indian temples. He and Hari hit it off at once – and they were soon deep in an exchange of views about

Somnathpur, a small Hoysala temple near Mysore, that I also happened to have visited. Simon couldn't find enough superlatives for it but Hari was less enthusiastic. He much preferred the overwhelming exuberance of the great temple at Madurai. "Madurai is quite magnificent" Simon conceded, "but it's just too much for a modern western eye. A bit like Iberian baroque. Not an inch that isn't saturated with intricate decoration. I can admire it, but it makes me long for some restraint. Somnathpur is, of course, also richly decorated, but the decoration doesn't overflow, and the whole place radiates tranquility in a way that Madurai doesn't – at least not for me." All this was a bit out of my depth but I couldn't resist chipping in to tell them what had moved me most about Somnathpur. It was the fact that in one corner of this Hindu temple there was a statue of the Buddha. Apparently Hinduism was flexible enough even then to incorporate in its temples the symbols of another faith. Hari did not find this surprising. "Once you regard your own gods as different incarnations of the one supreme being" he said "there is no great difficulty in accommodating other manifestations such as the Buddha or, for that matter, Jesus Christ." I could not help wondering whether the day would ever come when in the corner of one of our churches you might find a statue of Shiva dancing.

For all his devotion to India, Hari slowly took on the coloration of his new environment. I think the main catalyst of this change was Sita. Like all the other overseas scholars – Americans, Australians, South Africans – the newly arrived Indians naturally sought out their fellow countrymen and, at least initially, tended to pass their leisure hours in the company of the people whose background they shared. But this background encompassed many walks of life. Most of the Indian scholars came from educated, but not wealthy, families – the gifted children of academics, school teachers, civil servants – but there were also a few who came from a more prosperous, and even privileged, environment. Sita was the much-travelled daughter of a well-known Bombay tycoon and was then spending a rather leisurely three years with us in the hope that a degree in philosophy, politics, and economics might be obtained without too much effort. She was a very stylish creature who seemed to me to be completely westernised. The only vestige of traditional India that I could detect in her was a neat little bindi that she sometimes painted on her forehead in whatever colour matched the clothes she was wearing.

I was very surprised that Hari fell for her, but even more surprised that she took any interest in him. I suppose that for Hari it was simply a *coup de foudre*, but Sita must have sensed that there was something in him that she did not find in the other young men who pursued her. To look at, they made a rather incongruous couple – Hari a good head shorter than she was, sloppily dressed but with the face of an angel, and Sita all elegance and polish, with the dazzle of a film star. I first met her at an Indian restaurant where Hari had invited me, ostensibly to meet some of his friends. I thought that she had come with Ranjit, a handsome, self-confident young man whose father, I was told, had been a minister in one of Nehru's governments. The dinner was half over before I realized that she was with Hari and that this was his way of introducing her to me. It was at that dinner that I noticed that Hari was no longer a vegetarian. He had ordered a chicken tikka and ate it with relish.

Whatever other changes Sita produced in Hari she did not distract him from his work. Before his first year was out he was doing experiments on bacterial growth that were as good as any you could find. He worked with the dedication of a religious fanatic, and I would often find him still at it when, for one reason or another, I needed to come back to the laboratory late at night. Sometimes Sita would be there too, sitting demurely in a corner, immersed in a book. It cannot have been an easy role for her to play. One day Hari approached me rather shyly with a piece of paper in his hand. It was an advertisement for a research fellowship in one of our wealthier colleges. I was rather surprised that he should be interested in that sort of thing, for I still assumed, despite his progressive assimilation, that he was as eager as ever to return to India and resume his private war against leprosy. What's more, I rather doubted whether he would find a natural home in the conservative luxury of that particular place. But, of course, I assured him that if he did decide to put in an application, I would give it my strongest support.

I have always had serious reservations about the qualities that colleges look for in making elections of this kind. In the great majority of cases, the decision has to be taken on the basis of promise rather than achievement, and what counts for most is the impression that the candidate makes at interview. This means that the good actors usually come off best. I get tired of hearing college fellows claim that what they are looking for is "the spark of originality". My own view is that that spark cannot be detected at interview, and a long experience of the outcome of these interviews has merely served to deepen my scepticism. It was not that I thought Hari would be tongue-tied. On the contrary, I expected that if he were given half a chance he would go overboard in his eagerness to impress his audience. They, on the other hand, were very likely to view an excess of enthusiasm with suspicion, and they might then easily come to the conclusion that the candidate, however clever, would not make an agreeable colleague. And that is exactly what happened. Both Hari and I happened to know the man who was elected and neither of us had any doubt that he was a perfect mediocrity. Hari was very upset at the outcome and nothing I could say to him entirely dispelled the conviction that he had been rejected on racial grounds.

A few weeks later it was my turn to draw his attention to a fellowship that was being advertised. This time it was at a college where I thought he would have a very good chance of being elected. I knew the biologists there pretty well and thought that they would at least make an effort to explore Hari's candidature thoroughly if I provided them with the right kind of reference. Hari was very reluctant to put himself through the hoops again, but I urged him on, partly because he would need some form of financial support if he did not propose to return to India as soon as his scholarship expired – and a college fellowship was a very agreeable form of support – and partly because I wanted to convince him that we weren't all racists, as he had now begun to suspect. In the end, he agreed to put in an application, and I was very pleased when one of the biologists who would be interviewing him came to see me to get some further information. Well, the long and the short of it was that he was elected this time, and that initiated not only a wholesale transformation in his lifestyle but also, or so it seemed, a change in his character.

He was given rooms in college and found himself cosseted in a luxurious, almost aristocratic, environment where, even in his wildest dreams, he could never have imagined making his abode. He began to take a more than casual interest in food and to talk about wine as if it was a serious subject. As you might expect, he put on a little weight, and he sometimes turned up in clothes that were not exactly fashionable but that gave evidence of having been thought about. His conversation became progressively more worldly, and he couldn't resist letting me have his rather blasé comments about plays or exhibitions that he had seen in London. Sita must have been more than satisfied with the transformation and I guessed that she was encouraging it. In any case, she obviously took great pleasure in being the centre of attention at high table when Hari brought her in as his guest. None of this affected Hari's work. He remained totally committed to his experiments, and if he took a day off now and then to indulge his new-found cultural interests, he would make up for it by working round the clock the next day. But I had the impression that he was no longer working for the destitute lepers of India. He was working for himself.

I thought it was time for Hari to give his excellent experiments a public airing and managed to get him written into the programme of a conference on infectious diseases that was due to take place in London in the summer. He had never before lectured to a large audience and I had no doubt that he would need some drilling before the event. However, he didn't take at all kindly to the idea of a rehearsal, which he considered demeaning, and it was only after I became very heavy-handed that he finally agreed. Of course, he made the usual error of trying to cram much too much into the limited time available, he spoke too quickly, and he had no idea of what to do with lecture notes, blackboards, or slides. But by the end of a wearing afternoon, he was more or less licked into shape, and when, in due course, he presented his paper in London, it was very well received. So well received, in fact, that in the following week I had two letters from senior figures in the London medical scene asking whether Hari was on the market. I wasn't too sure what Hari's intentions now were, but I advised him against taking either of these propositions too seriously. The institutions concerned, though large, were undistinguished, and I had little doubt that he could obtain a much better position if, in the end, he decided not to return to India.

I had become accustomed to finding Sita in the corner of the laboratory if I came back in the evening, and when several weeks went by without my seeing her, I did not feel it to be too much of an intrusion to ask Hari where she was. "Sita" he replied "is a very superficial person. There are many assumptions about life that she and I do not share." That was all he was prepared to say, but it was enough to tell me that I was unlikely to see Sita again. I assumed, of course, that it was she who had walked out on him, and it was only months later that I learned, in the course of a chance encounter with one of his college friends, that it had been the other way round. But the corner of the laboratory in which Sita had sat reading did not remain unoccupied for long. One evening when I put my nose in, I found her place had been taken by a small round-faced blonde who was introduced to me as Cathy which was not, it turned out, an abbreviation of Catherine, but a substitute for Christine which she did not like. Cathy was a senior scholar at Hari's college, in the throes of producing a thesis on some aspect of Roman commerce with India. It was not unexpected that proximity and a community of interest should have brought Cathy and Hari together, but no one could have envisaged Cathy displacing Sita. Cathy was pleasant enough, but beside Sita she seemed to me to be very small beer. My guess was that Hari and Sita had already broken up before Cathy became a serious contender for the vacancy. And yet I couldn't avoid the impression that Hari's feelings for Cathy ran much deeper than they had for Sita. After the initial brief infatuation, Hari seemed to regard Sita mainly as an ornament, whereas with Cathy his speech was always courteous and his manner full of respect. I am not sure how long the Ganesha had been missing from Hari's desk before I noticed its absence; and I am not sure either whether it was the departure of the God that had allowed Cathy to enter Hari's life or whether it was her presence that had driven the God out; but that the removal of the Ganesha was a symbolic act of the deepest significance for Hari I had no doubt.

I did not see Cathy in the laboratory as often as I used to see Sita. No doubt she had her hands pretty full with her own research, but I could not help noticing that Hari had begun to include her in his long term plans in a way that he had never done with Sita. However, it was still not clear to me where Hari hoped that these long term plans would come to fruition. He was, indeed, given to bouts of irrational optimism, but I found it hard to believe that he could simply have ignored the difficulties that Cathy would have to overcome if she was to have any chance at all of finding acceptance in the communal life of Agra. On the other hand, he hadn't yet given me any firm indication that he now proposed to make his life with us. It took him a long time and a great deal of soul-searching before he could bring himself to confess that that was what he had finally decided to do. It came out one morning over coffee when he asked me, with acute embarrassment, whether I would help him find a suitable position when his college research fellowship expired. I told him that if he was at peace with the decision he had taken, I was more than willing to help. "No" he replied. "I am not at peace with my decision, and I doubt whether I ever will be, but any other decision would entail a sacrifice that I am simply unable to make."

My confidence that it would not be difficult to find Hari an attractive job was not misplaced. A month had hardly gone by when I received a letter from one of the more enlightened London medical schools asking me whether I could recommend someone for a newly created research position in the field of tropical medicine. They had apparently received an endowment for this purpose and were looking for a good experimentalist who could gather together and direct a small research group. The post seemed tailor-made for Hari, and I sent his name in with the strongest possible recommendation. I knew, of course, that Hari was not a lover of big cities, but I had the impression that he had now acquired a taste for London, or at least for some of the more pleasant things that London had to offer; and, in any case, the opportunity was, on the face of it, too good to miss. He was called for interview and came back bubbling with enthusiasm. A couple of weeks later he was offered the job.

I had never seen him in such high spirits. His head was full of plans for the future – what new lines of research he would initiate, how he would organise the work, where he would live – and at the centre of all these plans was Cathy. I hadn't spoken to Cathy often enough to be able to judge how closely her view of the future coincided with Hari's, but she didn't strike me as the kind of girl who would easily agree to give up her own ambitions for the sake of his. Indeed, I found it very disturbing that Hari, in his effervescent descriptions of his proposals, made no mention of what Cathy thought of it all, and when I asked him what arrangements had been made to ensure that Cathy could carry on her research, he was rather taken aback, almost as if he had never given the matter a moment's thought. It didn't seem to me to augur well for the future if Hari was assuming that Cathy would submissively adopt the role of a dutiful Hindu wife. Indeed, it even crossed my mind that Hari's long term plans for Cathy might not be plans at all but pipedreams that he hadn't yet discussed with her; or, worse still, that in the long term plans that she was making, there might be no place for Hari at all.

The blow fell sooner than I expected. A week or so after I questioned him about Cathy, Hari failed to turn up in the laboratory. He would usually let me know if he proposed to be away, or leave me a message if something unexpected had stopped him coming in. This time, however, there was no message and when, after he had been away for several days, I rang his college, I was told that he had been unwell and had gone off somewhere to recuperate. They didn't know where. When he turned up again, he was a changed man. His face, unshaven, was a mask of unrelieved gloom and, for the first time in many months, he was wearing his Indian clothes. Needless to say, I asked no questions, but after he had fiddled aimlessly for a while with his notebooks he simply said: "I am not going to take the job in London. I am going back to India." I did not attempt to dissuade him but did venture to suggest that it might be sensible to think things over for a bit before taking what might prove to be an irrevocable step. "I have done all the thinking I need to do" he replied. "I've spoken to the people in Agra and they are willing to have me back at any time. I've booked a flight to Delhi for the weekend after next." In the ensuing ten days I did not see much of him, although he did come into the laboratory from time to time to tidy things up. On his last Friday, late in the afternoon, he came in to say goodbye and to thank me for the help I had given him. He was a little tearful as he turned to go and then, without any prompting from me, he finally came out with it: "You do know, don't you, why I am leaving?" "I think so, Hari" I replied. He paused for a moment and, as if the world had come to an end, let the words fall: "She turned me down."

A few years later I was in India again. I had no special reason to go to Agra on this occasion but made a detour in order to see Hari once more. He had continued to send me reprints of his papers, and although his experiments were always of high quality, they didn't, I thought, quite fulfil the promise of his early work. The skill remained, but the passion seemed somehow to have evaporated. I took a plane that got me into Agra at dusk and Hari was there at the airport to meet me. There was no trace of the West in his appearance now. He wore a kurta and loose trousers, as he had on my first visit to Agra, but this time there were chappals instead of shoes; and he had grown a glossy black beard. It had been arranged that I should first be deposited at my hotel, and after I had had a chance to relax a little after what Hari assumed must have been a hard day, he would call again to take me to his home for dinner. As we rattled along the road from the airport in the institute car – the usual Hindustan Ambassador – I noticed in the half light that all the houses were decorated with flickering oil lamps. "What's all that for, Hari?" I asked. "Ah," he replied "You do not know? It is Diwali." As a matter of fact I did know – from the books – what the festival of Diwali was about, but I had never been to India at that time before and had no idea how romantically beautiful Indian streets can be when they are softly illuminated by countless small lamps. Nobody had told me that my itinerary would land me in Agra on that very day.

Diwali is, above all, a family festival, but Hari didn't seem to regard me as an intruder. He picked me up at the hotel as arranged, and we arrived at his modest home just as his wife Padma had finished her puja to Lakshmi and was giving Ashok and Indira, their two young children, their prasada of sweets. Padma was only a little taller than Hari and, being rather plump, had already acquired an air of almost middle-aged domesticity, but her face, like Hari's, was very beautiful, especially the liquid brown eyes that were full of gentleness. Ashok and Indira, resplendent in new clothes and glowing with cleanliness, were impatient to go out into the streets to see the illuminations, and Hari and I were deputed to take them on a tour of inspection while Padma put the last touches to our dinner. It was an elegant vegetarian meal on which she must have lavished great care. When it was over, and the children had finally been put to bed, Padma brought out a sitar and, settling herself cross-legged on a small rush mat, gave us a wonderfully nostalgic raga.

The next morning, at Hari's insistence, I visited his laboratory and exchanged a few words with his collaborators, but I had long ago seen all the laboratories I ever wanted to see, and since the director of the institute happened to be away, I was able to extricate myself pretty quickly without giving offence. Hari drove me to the airport and, as we said goodbye, he took a small parcel out of an old canvas bag that he was carrying and gave it to me. "It is a gift" he said, "but you must promise me that you will not open it until you get home."

As I sit at my desk writing these lines, a small stone Ganesha, with an infinitely contented paunch and a broken tusk, looks benignly at me from the other side of the room. I can't complain. Life hasn't treated me all that badly.

CHAPTER 10

THE ORDER OF NAMES

It is often said that an interest in the history of one's subject is, in a scientist, a sign of failing powers. If so, then my powers must have begun to fail very early, for I cannot remember a time, once I had learned to read for pleasure, when I was not fascinated by the personalities of those who had made great discoveries and by the circumstances in which those discoveries were made. So you'll find among my publications a number of occasional pieces in which some eminent scientist or some important scientific event is subjected to scrutiny, regrettably the far from expert scrutiny that lies within the purchase of a very amateur historian. Some of these pieces were prompted by invitations from editors in urgent need of an obituary notice or, less often, of a more extended biographical memoir. It was an invitation of this kind that set me to work on the scientific life of Basil D., who, some thirty years ago, had made a discovery whose importance can hardly be exaggerated. I remember being all but stunned by the paper when it appeared, for it showed, wholly unexpectedly and contrary to all our assumptions, that cells derived from our own bodies could somehow (we didn't find out how until very much later) exchange genes. Of course, such a revolutionary idea was received at first with extreme scepticism, but it was quickly confirmed and Basil was catapulted to a stardom that few scientists ever achieve.

I did not know him well, but well enough for us to be on first-name terms, and, having myself started out as a failed neuro-physiologist, I had followed his work in a desultory way for years. He was a specialist in the application of electrophysiological methods to the study of the nervous system, an approach that had been used with increasing technical sophistication for more than half a century and which readily lent itself to algebraic formulations that seemed to give great pleasure to practitioners of the art but which always struck me as no more than a substitute for an explanation. Basil's work was always thorough, indeed meticulous, and in the eyes of his orthodox colleagues he never put a foot wrong. As the years went by, his measurements became more and more precise and his algebra more and more exotic, but since he resolutely refused to allow his work to become molecular, nothing he did helped me to understand, in concrete terms, how even the simplest neurological processes actually worked. You couldn't help admiring the work, but I found it difficult to avoid the conclusion that it was, in the end, a form of shadow-boxing.

Scientific establishments are much more at ease with laudable extensions of ideas with which they are familiar than with genuine originality, and this is reflected in their system of rewards. Basil was made a Fellow of the Royal Society at an early age and was shortly afterwards elected into a professorship at one of the better London medical schools. There he succeeded in winning support for a sizeable research unit, and a stream of high-class papers along the lines of his own work soon began to flow from his department. It was a perfectly conventional success story, and I would have predicted that Basil, bored eventually with his scholastic science, would be translated at the appropriate time to some high academic office.

The personal records that I was given access to did reveal one or two unexpected details. I knew that Basil had been very expensively educated. In fact, the celebrated school that he had attended was perhaps the most expensive of all that sort of establishment, and it had left its mark. He was polite, indeed, for my taste, excessively so, but the slight drawl that he affected somehow conveyed an impression of detached superiority, and every now and again a snippet of private schoolboy slang would pop out, the kind of slang that served, and was intended to serve, as a form of identification. However, as far as I could judge, his parents must have been people of rather modest means. His father appeared to have spent the whole of his life in local government, but had never achieved a position of more than middling responsibility. There was no information at all about his mother's background, so I guessed that there was nothing too remarkable in it. His parents were not, in any case, the sort of people who could possibly have afforded to send Basil to that school out of their own resources. If he had won a scholarship, this would surely have received at least a mention in his personal record or in his entry in *Who's Who;* but there was no sign of it. Perhaps there had been a legacy of some sort. In any case, whatever the source of the finance, it was clear that Basil had spent his schooldays in the company of boys from much more affluent and socially prominent backgrounds than his own.

That might explain a streak of covert ruthlessness that was quite out of character with the personal style he had chosen to adopt but that I knew to be there. It's not too difficult to detect this. Small acts of ungenerous behaviour eventually give you away, but in Basil's case I had one piece of evidence that was decisive. Many years ago, a young Argentinian who was working with one of my colleagues had devised a useful little technique for making certain types of measurement at the cell membrane, and I had innocently drawn Basil's attention to this. You can imagine my outrage when, a few weeks later, in a journal that specialized in hurried publications, a short note appeared under Basil's name describing a simple variant of this same technique, but mentioning the young Argentinian, whose own paper had not yet appeared, only in a footnote which stated blandly that Basil's attention had been drawn to a rather similar procedure that had recently been devised. I was not then in a position to do anything other than fume, but I never again passed any information whatever to Basil.

I think Basil's marriage also had an element of ruthlessness in it. His wife was a plain, overweight and empty-headed woman whose twittering made nonsense of any conversation in which she was engaged, but she came with the substantial advantage of being the only child of a wealthy businessman who owned, among many other things, a string of petrol stations. This enabled Basil to live in a style that could never have been supported by any academic salary, but I think he paid a pretty high price for this. As he became more eminent, she became more pretentious, and I was certainly not alone in finding her insufferable.

The paper that assured Basil's place in the history of biology had three authors: Basil in front, one of his technicians, Caroline T., at the end and, sandwiched between them, L. M. Mermelshteyn. The work was astounding in many ways, but, in my eyes, the most surprising thing about it was that it had nothing to do with the electrophysiology to which Basil had diligently devoted years of his life and on which his solid reputation was based. Physiologists of Basil's kind tend to form a rather closed circle, and they rarely stray beyond the confines of their own technology. What's more, they are stout in the defence of their terrain, resisting any encroachments that might be attempted by geneticists, biochemists, and other molecular analysts. Often enough I had heard Basil, like many of his colleagues, describe his own approach to physiology as 'integrative', in contradistinction to more directly molecular approaches that he disparaged as 'disintegrative'. And here he was, with one totally unknown collaborator and a technician, diving head first into a molecular field that I would have assumed was *terra incognita* to him and emerging with a discovery that not only completely overshadowed everything he had previously done but that also gave evidence of profound insight into a wholly different technology. How could it have happened?

Well, Raphael might well have composed sonnets and Dante tried his hand at a portrait, but no stretch of my imagination could turn Basil into a Raphael or a Dante. It was, of course, possible, in principle, that the impetus, and the requisite methodological skills, might both have been provided by the enigmatic L. M. Mermelshteyn, but I thought this most unlikely, for two reasons. The first was that Basil's scientific collaborators were kept on a pretty tight leash and were certainly not encouraged to wander off into byways with which Basil was unfamiliar. It seemed to me to be wholly implausible that Basil would jettison his own well thought out research programme to accommodate a wild idea proposed by some transient visitor, but, in any case, the notion that Mermelshteyn might have been the key figure in the work was scotched by the order of the names on the paper. If the original idea had indeed been Mermelshteyn's, and especially if he had also been primarily responsible for the execution of the experiments, then his would have been the first name on the paper, and Basil would have appended his own name only at the end, to make it clear that the

139

work had come from his laboratory and that he had had a significant hand in it. But Basil's name at the head of the list of authors was a claim, well understood by his readership, that the crucial idea, or at least the crucial element in its success, was his, not Mermelshteyn's. It was this that I found so amazing. I did not underestimate Basil's intelligence or his technical skill or his ability to assimilate new information, but I could not see him as a source of volcanic originality, and that is exactly what that paper displayed. That Basil had been responsible, perhaps wholly responsible, for the actual writing of the paper I could well believe.

I heard Basil talk about the work a few weeks later at a meeting in London that I would not otherwise have attended. The lecture theatre was packed out and I found myself sitting on a stair in one of the aisles. Basil was immensely impressive. It was not at all the kind of performance you might expect from a departmental head giving a generalised, but not deeply understood, account of the work of one of his junior colleagues. Basil was completely on top of every aspect of his subject – the specialized language, the technical detail and the deeper implications. As his talk drew to a close, I found it difficult to resist the conclusion that there must, after all, be much more to Basil than I had hitherto imagined; and I think all my doubts would have been dispelled but for one small thing. Sitting jammed beside me in the aisle there was a small, rather battered-looking man who kept shaking his head all the way through Basil's lecture. I would have guessed that he was close to forty for his wispy hair was quite grey, but people on whose faces life has written a depressing story often seem much older than they are. His clothes were shabby, not with the shabbiness that comes from long wear, but intrinsically shabby, as if made that way from the beginning; and when, now and again, he opened his mouth, I saw the gleam of two stainless steel teeth. It was only behind the Iron Curtain that they made teeth like that, so I wasn't at all surprised to hear, when he finally spoke to me at the end of the lecture, that he had the thickest of Russian accents. I had no reason to believe that he had any idea who I was, and I suppose that I was chosen simply because I was there. All he said was: "It iss a disgrace, vot he iss doink", and then he stormed off. Needless to say, it was not at all clear to me what I was expected to do about this disgrace but, for one brief moment, there flickered across my mind the disturbing thought that the angry man with the stainless teeth might conceivably be L. M. Mermelshteyn. Many years were to go by before I found out.

Basil's discovery was rapidly colonized; indeed it would not be an exaggeration to say that it gave rise to a new industry. Under such circumstances it often happens that the original discovery is submerged in an avalanche of secondary publications and, up to a point, that happened to Basil, but his primacy was nonetheless widely recognized and, for a year or two, he became a celebrity on the international lecture circuit. That was long enough for him to win a couple of serious international prizes and to assure his election to some foreign academies. His lectures were always models of lucidity and were delivered with great style, but, as far as I could see, there was no evidence in them that he had personally developed the work beyond the stage that he had originally described, although, of course, he was more than adept in incorporating in his exposition the important findings made by others. If you have nothing new to say, conference organisers quickly drop you from their programmes, and I was not too surprised that Basil's dominance of the lecture circuit in his new-found subject turned out to be pretty short-lived. Indeed, it seemed to me that he returned to his own brand of neurophysiology with some relief. It was almost as if the great discovery with which his name will always be associated was no more than a parenthesis in his life – a momentary aberration in an otherwise predictable and tranquil career.

As time went by he became increasingly involved in the higher reaches of academic administration, and I never heard anything but praise for his impartiality, judgement, and tact. Among the scientific politicians of his generation, there can have been few who were more influential. His name continued to appear on serious experimental papers, but I had the impression that science was something he now did with his left hand. I confidently expected that he would soon receive an invitation to a highly desirable Vice-Chancellorship and that he would accept it. But the Fates are blind. I would never have picked him as a candidate for a fatal coronary occlusion at the unreasonably early age of fifty-five. He was tall, lean, and moved with the easy grace of an athlete who had not allowed himself to go to seed. In fact, I knew that he was a more than respectable squash player, and only the closest scrutiny would reveal the few white strands in the shock of black hair that he brushed straight back from his forehead. It was not at all clear to me that I was an appropriate choice to provide a biographical memoir. It would have been better done, I thought, by one of the neurophysiologists, but I suppose the invitation came to me because Basil's great fame rested not so much on his work in neuro-physiology but on that amazing parenthetical discovery that did indeed fall more naturally within my own field of interest than within the traditional confines of neurophysiology. In any event, a formal invitation to write a memoir of one of your colleagues is difficult to decline, even if you are not unreservedly enthusiastic about the idea.

In the year that followed the appearance of Basil's great paper, I noticed two further communications that bore the name of L. M. Mermelshteyn. Mermelshteyn must have left Basil's laboratory pretty quickly, for the new work emanated from Pierre C.'s laboratory in Paris. Pierre was a well known figure in the French academic scene and had for many years directed the work of an energetic group of collaborators. His was one of the many laboratories that moved quickly to exploit the possibilities opened up by Basil's paper. The first of the two communications bearing Mermelshteyn's name was brief and represented little more than a routine extension of the earlier work. In the list of four authors, Mermelshteyn's name came first and Pierre C.'s last, so it was reasonable to suppose that Mermelshteyn had taken the technique to Pierre's laboratory where it was rapidly developed. In the second communication, which was a good deal more interesting, Pierre had put his own name first and Mermelshteyn's was rather lost in the midst of a sizeable list of other collaborators. After that Mermelshteyn's name did not again come to my notice, and a systematic search of the literature that I made some years later confirmed that he had vanished without trace.

I did not think I would get much cooperation from Basil's widow when I asked for access to his scientific correspondence and his laboratory notebooks. But, to my surprise, she was very willing to let me look at whatever I wanted. It was obvious that she had no doubts at all about her late husband's permanent place in history, and she was already busy guiding the hands of future historians. She clearly did not envisage the possibility that there could be anything in his scientific papers that might cast a shadow on his impeccable reputation. Basil's laboratory notes were a model of orderly precision. It was not at all difficult to see why a particular experiment was undertaken and exactly how it had turned out, but all the experiments recorded so meticulously in Basil's own hand were variations on the classical themes of neurophysiology to which Basil had always remained faithful. There was not a single note in his own hand that gave evidence of his having been involved at all in the experimental work that produced the paper on gene transfer. Indeed, in the year that preceded the appearance of that paper, there was a period of some three months when there were no laboratory notes at all. If Basil was indeed personally involved in the experiments on gene transfer and if, in his usual orderly fashion, he made notes on them, then those notes had not been clipped into the folders that contained all his other work; and although I made a thorough search, I could not find them anywhere else. Basil's correspondence had not yet been properly sorted, so it was quite a tedious task to find any letters that might shed light on the period of three months silence during which there were no laboratory notes. But eventually I found what I was looking for. It transpired that Basil had arranged to spend those three months in the USA, for the most part in Boston where he had colleagues whose work was closely relevant to his own, but also briefly at some other academic centres where he proposed to give lectures or seminars. I asked his widow about this trip, but she could not recall it with any certainty as there had been so many over the years. When the time came for me to thank her for her cooperation, I could not help feeling a little treacherous.

I never quite lost track of Caroline T., Basil's former technician. She had married one of our physicists and I came across her now and again as she did her shopping in the centre of town, sometimes with two attractive children in tow. I can recall one occasion when we were thrown together at some official function to which both her husband and I had been invited, and another when we happened to sit next to each other at a dinner party. I formed the impression that she was a sensible and discreet woman who would not easily be induced to gossip about her former employer; and I was not at all optimistic that I would be able to get much out of her about Basil's doings in the critical year that preceded the publication of his celebrated paper. But I now had the bit between my teeth and felt that it was at least worth a try. So I rang her at home one evening and explained my predicament. Here I was, saddled with the task of writing an official biographical memoir for Basil, with most of his work barely within my grasp and the circumstances that generated his great paper on gene transfer totally obscure. Could she help me? She was at first rather reluctant, claiming to have only a hazy recollection of what had gone on at the time, but then I think it dawned on her that a blank refusal to provide any information at all was in itself more revealing than she perhaps intended. Hesitantly, she asked me whether I could come to tea the following Sunday afternoon.

We were joined by her husband, and I guessed at once that they had already discussed the matter and come to a decision. I had always found him to be an independent and straightforward person and I think he must have prevailed upon her to set aside her natural discretion and tell me frankly what she knew. I began by asking her about Mermelshteyn. "Ah, Leonid Moiseievitch" she exclaimed, playing with the conventional Russian patronymic, "he was one of the most colourful characters I ever met. Always bubbling over with fantastic suggestions and quite impossible to control. He came to us from Moscow, you know, and his English was quite bizarre. We were never too sure whether he really did intend to do what he said or whether we had simply misunderstood him. I don't know how it came about that he fetched up in our lab. For he had no background in neurophysiology, and, as far as I could see, not much interest in the subject. He was a geneticist by training, and from the day he arrived he talked obsessionally about genes, although I must confess that I didn't understand one word of what he was saying. Basil had great difficulty with him to begin with, because he didn't want to work on the project that Basil had in mind, but he did eventually knuckle under, or at least gave the appearance of doing so. If you wanted to stay in Basil's lab there was no other way. Leonid was not much good with his hands, and I remember one occasion when he broke an expensive piece of equipment and brought Basil's wrath down on his head."

Caroline's recall of detail was, in fact, very impressive, and I did not once interrupt her as she built up her vivid picture of Leonid, but when she eventually paused to take breath I asked her point blank: "Whose idea was it to see whether the cells of the body could exchange genes?". "Oh" she answered, "there's no doubt about that. Leonid was talking about that sort of thing from the day he arrived, but Basil, more than sceptical, never let him off the leash. It wasn't until Basil went off on a tour of the United States that Leonid managed to get together what he needed to try the experiment, and I can never forget his uncontrollable excitement at the way it turned out."

"When Basil got back he was furious and at first wouldn't look at the data that Leonid kept pressing on him. But eventually he relented and then he was not slow to grasp the significance of what had been done. However, he didn't have much faith in Leonid's experimental competence and at once wanted the whole thing repeated. That's where I came in. Basil insisted that I help Leonid with the work, not because there was much call for technical assistance, but because Basil wanted someone whom he trusted to monitor everything Leonid did. And Basil himself watched us like a hawk at every stage of the operation. Well, the results turned out just as before, but cleaner. At that point Basil took off. I think he was just as excited as Leonid but, of course, with him it was all kept under rigid control. It was Basil who wrote up the paper. I don't think Leonid could have constructed an intelligible paragraph in English, perhaps not in Russian either. And it was Basil who gave all the lectures." I interrupted her to ask how Leonid had reacted to that. "To begin with he didn't seem to mind," she said "for I think he realised that he was not himself up to it. But gradually it dawned on him that Basil was taking the whole business out of his hands. He began to complain that he was not being given the credit that was due to him and he ended up calling Basil a thief. I think there was some trouble, too, about the order of the names on the paper. One day Leonid simply failed to turn up, and a couple of weeks later we heard that he was working in a lab in Paris."In his position" I observed "that can't have been easy to arrange. Was he married?" "Oh yes," she replied "and he had a child too. But he told us that they would never let his wife out of Russia while he was abroad." At that point Caroline left to bring in the tea and, as we sat nibbling the cucumber sandwiches, her husband, who until then had been silent, turned to me and asked in his usual forthright manner: "It isn't a pretty story, is it? What are you going to write?" "I'm not sure." I replied. "Perhaps nothing."

And, indeed, I was now faced with a very difficult choice. If Caroline's account of what had happened was anywhere near the truth and not simply a reflection of what Leonid had persuaded her to believe, then Basil's fame rested on his having purloined the ideas and the work of another man. I could hardly put that into an official biographical memoir, and, in any case, was my evidence really strong enough to warrant my making so destructive an accusation? Might not there be another version of events, one that Basil's death had now rendered inaccessible. I could, of course, compromise, leaving the emperor with some of his clothes but giving due weight to Mermelshteyn's contribution; but that, it seemed to me, was the sort of compromise that compounded the injustice. It might well be that I would never be able to establish the truth of the matter with any certainty; but the more I turned the options over in my mind, the clearer it became that the one thing I could not do was write a biographical memoir that was a fake.

It so happened that I had business to do in Paris that year. One of the Paris publishing houses that specialized in medical and scientific publications had decided to produce a French version of a book I had written, and the editor in charge of the project had asked whether I could find the time to come over and discuss some items that were giving him difficulty. I don't need much inducement to go to Paris, and a few days after my conversation with Caroline I fixed a date. What determined that date was not my own convenience nor that of my editor but the availability of Pierre C. with whom Mermelshteyn had worked after he left Basil's laboratory. In the past I had always found it almost impossible to pin Pierre down to a particular time and place. Whenever I thought that an arrangement involving him had finally be settled, he was inevitably called away at the last minute to attend some crucially important meeting which always seemed to be convened at short notice. What's more, he was incurably addicted to scientific tourism in remote places so that, for most of the year, it was not easy even to make contact with him. This time I was pleasantly surprised to find not only that he was available on most of the days I suggested, but that he seemed actually to welcome the opportunity of spending an hour or two with me. I learned later that he had finally been forced to retire, and I suppose that he now had time on his hands. I suggested dinner at La Chope d'Alsace which was only a few minutes walk from my hotel in the rue Madame, and he thought that was a good idea.

When the Gewürztraminer had warmed us up, I asked him how he had managed to winkle Mermelshteyn out of Basil's laboratory. "No, no" he said, "it wasn't like that at all. It was he who wrote to me to ask not only whether I could accommodate him but also whether I could find some funds to sustain him. I had met him after one of Basil's lectures in London and I confess that I did indeed invite him to visit us, for I had decided as soon as I heard about the work that we would take it up in our lab also. But I had in mind no more than a visit. It was not at all my intention to poach him. However, in his letter to me he did not hide the fact that he was far from happy in Basil's lab and he was obviously hoping that I would bail him out. Well, I did bail him out. It was not all that easy to get a French visa and a work permit for a Soviet citizen who was not coming to France under official auspices – who was, as you would say, on the loose – and I had to pull some pretty subtle strings to get it done quickly. But somehow it was done, and within a few weeks of his arriving in our lab he had shown that the gene transfer described in that famous paper was not a *bizarrerie* exhibited by one unusual cell type but was a quite general phenomenon. For this he used systems that we had developed in our lab., and, after that, several of my colleagues jumped in to exploit the situation. Leonid was reluctant to join in this further extension of the work, although he did make some contribution to it. He had a very aristocratic view of science and regarded the mere elaboration or exploitation of a discovery as beneath him. He often used the word 'second order' not in any technical sense, but simply as a term of disparagement. There was some other revolutionary idea with which he was now obsessed, but before he could get round to trying it out, he was hauled back to the USSR, and we never saw him or heard of him again."

147

"Do you think" I asked "that the whole idea of looking for gene transfer in that way was his?" "I think that's very likely. I can see Basil tidying up a bit, but Basil, of all people, generating a revolutionary idea in a field that he knew nothing about is unbelievable. Anyhow, Leonid always claimed not only that the idea was his, but that it was he, not Basil, who did the experiment. Indeed, he said that he had done it while Basil was away. He never ceased to complain that Basil had stolen his work, but my guess would be that the precision of what finally appeared must have owed something to Basil, because Leonid in the lab. was a monument of sloppiness." We were given an excellent meal, and to finish it off Pierre had two substantial glasses of cognac with the result that we went on talking for much longer than I had intended; and before the evening was over I was given an insight into the private lives of several notable figures in the Paris scientific scene. As we were going in opposite directions we parted company outside the restaurant, but, after I had taken a couple of steps, I turned round and watched him for a moment or two, swaying happily off into the night.

By the time I got back from Paris I had finally made up my mind. I sent off a letter to say that, although I had already invested a good deal of my time in the project, I was regrettably quite unable to produce an acceptable biographical memoir for Basil. I gave two reasons. The first was that my understanding of Basil's brand of neurophysiology was too superficial to permit me to do justice to what was, after all, the bulk of his life's work. And the second was that, despite extensive enquiries, I still could not fathom how it had come about that Basil was able to make a great discovery in a field that was totally alien to him and in which he had previously shown no interest whatever. The biographical memoir that eventually appeared was written by one of his physiological colleagues. It was a hagiographic piece that stressed not only the precision that made Basil an impeccable neurophysiologist in the classical tradition, but also the intellectual flexibility that enabled him to make a historic contribution to the study of genetics.

Had this account of my enquiry into Basil's discovery been written a couple of years ago, it would have ended at this point. Once I had finally decided not to write that biographical memoir, I had little reason to give either Basil or Leonid Moiseievitch Mermelshteyn much thought. But a wholly unexpected turn of events last year brought the matter into sharp focus again. I had received an invitation to give some lectures in Israel, at the Weizmann Institute in Rehovot and at the Hebrew University in Jerusalem. I chose the month of October to catch some pleasant weather, and after I had done my duty and had been lavishly entertained, I decided to look up an old school friend who, when last I heard from him, lived in Haifa. He had been an ardent Zionist in his youth and had settled in Israel soon after taking his medical degree. His name was Melman and when I looked him up in the English language telephone directory, I noticed, a little below the Melmans, two Mermelsteins and a Mermelshteyn. Now Mermelstein, however spelt, was one of the many grotesque identities that the Tsarist authorities had imposed on their Jewish subjects, and the unusual transliteration of the name that Leonid had adopted for the paper that he published with Basil and Caroline was no doubt an attempt to guide English-speaking readers towards some semblance of the correct pronunciation of the name in Russian. I therefore thought it rather unlikely to be mere coincidence that there should be someone living in Hovevei Zion Street Haifa who chose to spell the English version of their name in just that way. It was, in any case, worth at least a phone call to find out, even if communication depended critically on the recipient of my call having at least a modicum of English.

Tamara Mermelshteyn lived with an aged aunt in a small flat halfway up Hovevei Zion Street. She had answered my telephone call in hesitant, but easily comprehensible, English, marked not by the gutteral Rs of modern Hebrew but by softer inflections that, to my ear, had an unmistakeably Russian origin. Yes, she was indeed the wife of the Leonid Mermelshteyn who had visited England many years ago and worked on gene transfer. And yes, she would be very pleased to see me and to let me have further details about the life and work of her late husband. So I made arrangements to spend an extra day in Haifa and on a mellow Sunday afternoon at four o'clock I arrived at her front door with a small bunch of autumn flowers in my hand.

She was a small, stocky woman with a face that reminded me of photographs of Marie Curie, but endowed with even greater severity by the fact that she wore her straight iron-grey hair in a bob. She led me into a small living room, and it was as if I had entered a modest Moscow apartment in the 1930s. There was not the slightest sign of modern Israeli ornamentation. The pictures on the walls were hackneyed prints of Russian paintings showing birch trees in the snow, the red silk lampshades had long fringes, and in the corner of the room there stood a samovar. I was introduced to her aunt who gave every indication of being an archetypal Russian babushka, with smooth silver hair pulled back into a bun. She spoke no English, but had made some 'zakuski' to have with our tea, which we drank with lemon out of tall glasses. When tea was over and the aunt had disappeared, Tamara fetched a large wooden box (also made of birch, I thought) containing a collection of documents and a few photographs. A glance at the latter confirmed that Leonid Mermelshteyn was indeed the man with the stainless steel teeth who had sat beside me at Basil's lecture. And then, without emotion but with great attention to detail, Tamara let me have the whole story.

She and Leonid had met as biology students in the same class at Moscow University and had married soon after graduation. He had been a very gifted student, but rather unmanageable, and although his talents were recognized by his teachers, he gave them too much trouble for him ever to become a favourite pupil. It was during the days of Lysenko's dominance of Russian biology, and the university courses, especially those dealing with genetics and evolution, were taught within the straitjacket of a doctrine called Michurinism, named after a successful practical plant breeder of an earlier generation. Leonid, even as a student, had nothing but contempt for Lysenkoism or Michurinism and spent a good deal of his time ferreting out important papers in classical genetics, which was a difficult and risky thing to do at that time. For his doctoral work he contrived to be taken on by a professor who had been a pupil of Vavilov, the famous geneticist who had suffered martyrdom at Stalin's hands. While he was still a doctoral student, Leonid had circulated in samizdat a theoretical paper on possible mechanisms of gene transfer. Regrettably Tamara no longer had a copy of that. With the fall of Khrushchev, Lysenko and his doctrines rapidly lost their stranglehold on Russian biological science, and many geneticists who had clung precariously to their posts by suppressing the views they held began once more to reassert classical Mendelian doctrines. But an even more wonderful development in the eyes of young Russian scientists was the emergence of the possibility that at least a few of them might be permitted to travel abroad.

This was a dream that had haunted Leonid for years, but he knew that his chances were vanishingly small. The director of the institute in which Leonid worked, Academician Professor P., was no friend. He was a physiologist who disliked geneticists on principle and disliked Leonid in particular because he was too gifted, because he was unruly, and especially because he was a Jew. But Professor P. was also a very agile politician, and he had managed to stay afloat through all the perilous academic storms that Stalin and Khrushchev had unleashed. It was never clear why Professor P. had proposed Leonid for an academic visit abroad, but Tamara thought that this too might have been a piece of opportunism. With Mendelian geneticists once more in the ascendant, it might have been in his own long term interest to put forward someone like Leonid. But Professor P. had a jaundiced view of the genetical laboratories in the West that Leonid chose. He thought they were places where there was too much excited talk and not enough devotion to experimental precision. He took the view, which, up to a point, Tamara shared, that what Leonid needed was not a flow of new ideas, but some thorough training in practical laboratory disciplines. It turned out that Professor P. had met Basil, was a great admirer of his work, and was convinced that Basil's laboratory was the ideal destination for Leonid. Leonid protested that he did not know Basil as a geneticist, did not, in fact, know him at all, but it was Basil or nothing. So, of course, Leonid eventually agreed. As was inevitable at the time, Tamara had to stay behind, as a kind of hostage, but Leonid wrote to her regularly.

He was deeply disappointed in Basil and regarded the work done in his laboratory as pedantic and sterile. Apparently Basil had no interest at all in any of the ideas that Leonid brought with him from Moscow, and Leonid found it especially frustrating that he was given no opportunity to try out the experiment he had devised to explore the possibility that body cells might exchange genes. He was fast coming to the conclusion that his trip to the West would prove

151

to be a complete waste of time, when an unexpectedly cheerful letter to Tamara announced the welcome news that Basil was off to the United States for three months and that this might give Leonid a chance to try the experiment that dominated his imagination. There followed a couple of brief notes describing the progress of the work, and then an ecstatic letter announcing the spectacular result. At this point Tamara interrupted her orderly narrative and took out of the birchwood box some battered papers covered with a chaos of jottings and diagrams. The barely legible text was a mishmash of English and Russian, but, with Tamara's help, I was easily able to see that these were Leonid's laboratory notes; and, as most of them were dated, it was clear to me that the work had indeed been done during Basil's absence, for the date of Basil's departure for the United States and the date of his return were graven in my memory. Tamara's account of what happened after Basil's return largely confirmed what Caroline T. had told me. As it dawned on Leonid that Basil was systematically appropriating the credit for the work, his letters to Tamara became vituperative, almost incoherent; and although she had warned him that it might be perilous to decamp to Paris, he was not to be deterred. According to Tamara, Leonid eventually came to the conclusion that Pierre C. was not much better than Basil, from which I inferred that Leonid's contribution to the interesting paper on which Pierre had appeared as first author might well have been much greater than I had previously assumed.

Tamara had given me everything I had come for, and I had no right to pry; but I simply couldn't resist asking her what had happened when Leonid returned to Moscow, for my search of the literature had not revealed any mention of his name after that date. For a moment or two Tamara made no reply, and it seemed to me that the composure that had marked her behaviour until then suddenly gave way. "It is a very sad story" she said. And indeed it was, as sad as any I had ever heard. When Leonid returned to Moscow he could convince no-one that it was he who was primarily responsible for the work described in Basil's already famous paper. Professor P. preened himself on his wisdom in having sent Leonid to Basil and was naturally very pleased to have had someone from his institute associated with the great work, even if in a subordinate capacity. He was incensed at Leonid's version of what had happened and strongly advised him not to make such improbable and transparently self-seeking claims. So Leonid was forced to accept that there was nothing he could safely do to rectify the injustice; but he never really came to terms with it. Tamara then went on to say that as long as she had known him, there had been periods when Leonid's habitual enthusiasm was displaced by deep gloom, and shortly after his return to Moscow, he had fallen victim to one of these black episodes. But it was not the theft of his discovery that had precipitated the bout of depression; his reaction to that was essentially anger. What broke his spirit was a catastrophe of a quite different order.

A few months before Leonid's departure for the West, Tamara had given birth to a child, Mischa, who at once became for Leonid a source of great joy and a hope for the future. But during Leonid's absence abroad it became clear to Tamara that Mischa was not developing as he should. She was given reassurance, but no satisfactory explanation, by the doctor to whom she took the child and, no doubt mistakenly, she had decided that there was no point in worrying Leonid with her vague sense of unease. However, by the time he returned it was clear that Mischa's head was much bigger than it ought to be, that his eyesight was impaired, and that he had completely lost interest in his surroundings. Leonid managed to arrange a consultation with a well-known paediatrician in one of the university clinics, and then, at last, the devastating truth came out. Mischa had Tay-Sachs disease, an inherited disorder that was invariably fatal within the first two or three years of life. Tamara knew that this otherwise rare genetic disease was much more common among the Ashkenasi Jews of Eastern Europe and Russia, but she explained that the precise biochemical tests used in the West to facilitate diagnosis were not available in the USSR, and no attempts at all were made to screen for carriers of the defective gene as both she and Leonid turned out to be. Leonid's depression deepened as Mischa's life drew to a close, and although he managed to struggle to work on most days, it was clear that his heart was not in it. Late one afternoon, when Tamara came back from a meeting at the school where she was employed as a biology teacher, she found Leonid hanging from one of the rafters that held up the ceiling in their dilapidated bathroom.

Tamara did not remarry. She soldiered on from one year to the next, but a name as obviously Jewish as Mermelshteyn was more than a trivial impediment to her career as a teacher. When Gorbachev finally decided to allow Jews to emigrate to Israel, she applied for a visa and, after the usual byzantine bureaucratic delays, eventually got one. Her aunt, who had been brought to a mandated Palestine by her parents in the 1920s, now lived alone, so Tamara was luckier than most immigrant Russian Jews in finding somewhere agreeable to live. But her knowledge of Hebrew was rudimentary, and she soon gave up all hope of finding employment that was anything like commensurate with the level of her education and training. She now had a menial job at the Haifa Technion and was grateful for that. I was so absorbed in what I was being told that I lost all track of time, and it was long past nightfall when I finally rose to go. Tamara asked me what I proposed to do with the information she had given me. I said that I was not sure, but felt that, at the very least, I would write something that gave Leonid the credit that was his due. We shook hands and said goodbye. I have not seen or heard from her since.

There is a rumour going about that they are thinking of naming a new research institute after Basil. What am I to do?

CHAPTER 11

RETIREMENT

Often, on summer evenings, I take a stroll after dinner to see what's happening in the suburban gardens that surround this house that I have lived in for more than a quarter of a century. Gardens can tell you a great deal about the people who tend them, sometimes more than you have a right to know. At one extreme there are the manicured plots with no blade of grass out of place and symmetrical herbaceous borders stocked with the platitudes of the gardening world. At the other, there are the layers of concrete that stifle the generous earth to provide parking space for motor cars.

Within the ambit of my evening walks there was no garden more meticulous or more orthodox than Cedric P.'s. Cedric and his wife Elizabeth had been friends of mine since time immemorial. I remember him first as a gifted and ambitious young medievalist, then as a middle-aged conscientious tutor who had somehow got bogged down in college administration, and finally as an ageing scholar whose infrequent articles on village life in medieval England were always regarded as impeccable, but, taken together, didn't quite add up to what he and others had hoped he would achieve. Elizabeth didn't give him much room for manoeuvre. I think she was basically a timid woman, but her timidity took the form of rigid adherence to a rather outmoded set of conventions that so constrained their behaviour and their conversation that it was difficult to avoid seeing them as a caricature. Tea with Elizabeth and Cedric was an excursion into an age long gone by; and you had to be very circumspect if your remarks went much beyond the weather. As Cedric approached retirement, Elizabeth's health began to give cause for concern. I am not quite sure what the illness was, but it seemed to give Cedric a new mission in life, for he began to fuss over her as if she were an invalid, when, as far as I could see, there was as yet no sign that she was unable to cope perfectly well herself. At the farewell dinner that his friends had arranged for him, he was subjected to the usual laudatory speeches, but Elizabeth's prim presence seemed to inhibit any display of the warmth that many of us certainly felt.

The reactions of academics to retirement are rarely temperate. There are those who cling to whatever privileges remain at their disposal and strive to participate even more eagerly than before in the social and intellectual life of the community in which they have spent their working lives. And then there are those who lay down their burden with immense relief and are rarely seen again. Cedric fell squarely into the latter category. If we had not lived close by, I doubt whether our paths would ever again have crossed. Elizabeth didn't much like his academic colleagues and was, I think, rather intimidated by them. In any case, she studiously avoided academic occasions where her presence would normally have been expected and where there is no doubt that she would have been welcome. In fact, I gathered from the comments that she sometimes made that she even resented the odd occasion when Cedric was more or less obliged to dine in college without her. My impression was that she rather looked forward to the prospect of detaching him from university life altogether.

I do not in the least wish to imply that there wasn't much wrong with Elizabeth's health, but she certainly enjoyed being the undivided centre of Cedric's solicitous attention, and the more he treated her as an invalid, the more she became one. Cedric did all the shopping. I knew this because on my way home from work I often called at the small supermarket down the road to pick up a carton of milk or a loaf of bread or something else that we happened to have run out of, and there I would see Cedric working his way methodically through the shelves and checking the sell-by date of every item. Sometimes we came upon each other in the public lending library, where he regularly borrowed as many volumes as he and Elizabeth were allowed, but, as far as I could see, they were all travel books or fiction. The travel books must have been for Cedric, for he had told me on one occasion that he didn't read contemporary fiction, and on another that he would quite like to see some more of the world, but didn't now think it would be possible. If, on one of my evening walks, I found him in his front garden, we would always exchange a few words, and then he would ask me whether I thought that a tender azalea that he intended to plant would survive an English winter, or whether my lawn was as badly plagued by moss this year as his was. Once or twice, in the hope of striking a spark, I asked him some contrived question about one or other of the articles he had written, but his laconic reply led me to suppose that the medieval English village was now far from his thoughts.

Elizabeth died a completely avoidable death. Whatever the illness was that had made a semi-invalid of her, that wasn't what killed her. She had been turning over the soil in a window box with a small gardening fork when her hand slipped and one of the prongs of the fork pierced the palm of her other hand. It was apparently a rather deep wound, but she did no more than wash it out and cover it with sticking plaster. About a week later, the first spasms of tetanus made their appearance and three days after that, despite every kind of intensive care, she was dead. The funeral service was held in the little church that adjoins our local shopping centre, and she was buried in the nearby cemetery where Cedric had long ago reserved a double plot. Only a handful of people came to the funeral, mainly neighbours as far as I could see. Elizabeth and Cedric had no children, and if any of her own family were still alive, they weren't in evidence on that sad day. Of Cedric's former academic colleagues, there were only two that I could recognise.

I see that I haven't yet told you what Cedric looked like. I must do that now because after Elizabeth's death, his appearance began to change. He rather resembled David Niven, or perhaps more closely Ronald Colman, for those who remember him. There was the same dapper air, the neat little moustache, the modest charm, but whereas these graces in the case of David Niven and Ronald Colman served as a form of camouflage to conceal a deeply unconventional inner life, in Cedric's case they appeared to conceal nothing at all. His dark brown hair, not as curly as Niven's but wavier than Colman's, was always neatly combed and was never allowed to grow too long. It slowly turned grey as the years went by, but his moustache and his eyebrows remained dark, which introduced a note of disharmony in an otherwise unremarkable face. I cannot remember seeing him without a tie except when he was working in his garden, and even then the bared neck was concealed by a discreet silk scarf. The clothes he usually wore were old enough to appear aristocratic, but not so old as to be shabby. The first sign of change that I noticed was when I saw him working in his garden with shirt collar unbuttoned, but no silk scarf, and it seemed to me that his hair had grown a little longer than Elizabeth would ever have permitted. I asked him on that occasion whether he proposed to get someone in from time to time to help him with the housework, but he replied that he didn't think that was necessary, at least not for the time being. He changed his mind pretty quickly, because a few weeks later I noticed in the window of the shop where I buy my newspapers a small card on which Cedric was offering excellent pay and conditions for part-time domestic help. The advertisement must have brought him someone whom he thought suitable, for the next time I passed by his house there was a young woman sweeping out the front porch.

I eventually got to know Sarah quite well, so I can tell you something of her background. She had been brought up in Sheffield by her mother and grandmother who together ran a small sweet-shop in one of the city's grimy back streets. She had never known her father and was not, in fact, too sure who he was. I gathered from what she told me that she hadn't had any difficulty with her school work, but she complained that she had found it all rather dull. As you might have predicted, it was in the life of the streets that she found her natural habitat and, as soon as she was old enough, in the hothouse culture of the discos. She left school just as soon as the law allowed and, after drifting around Sheffield for a few months, made her way to London. What happened there was never too clear to me, but I don't suppose it made a pretty story. One of our graduate students had picked her up somewhere in London and had brought her back to share his digs. She lived with him for the best part of a year, making a little money now and again in odd jobs that she managed to find. Then he had gone off and she was left once again to her own devices. When she replied to Cedric's advertisement she was having difficulty in finding her rent.

She was a rather stocky girl with straight fair hair cropped short around a squarish face, and when I first saw her sweeping out the porch she was wearing patched jeans and a black polo-necked sweater. She and Cedric must have hit it off, because I once saw them working in the garden together, and I was sure that Cedric would not have permitted that unless he had found her company agreeable. The garden, like Cedric himself, began to change. It was rather as if a Canaletto painting was slowly dissolving into a Monet. The rigid symmetry of the flower beds gave way to softer contours and the shrubs that had previously been trimmed into submission were now allowed to riot a little. This change couldn't have come from Sarah, who had never had much access to a garden, but must have been imposed by Cedric himself; and since his hair was now long enough to curl slightly over his neck and he was often to be seen at the shopping centre in an anorak and trainers, I concluded that what I saw taking place in the garden was simply a part of the metamorphosis that was gradually releasing a new Cedric from the old. I must say that I viewed all this with pleasure, for I had a very bleak view of what the future had in store for Cedric, encased as he was in a straitjacket of infinite boredom. It was the death of Elizabeth, and not the arrival of Sarah, that had initiated the unexpected renaissance, but if Sarah's presence contributed in some measure to the process that seemed to me to be all to the good. But when I learned that Sarah had finally moved in with Cedric, I began to have my doubts. Was this not, after all, a classic recipe for disaster?

Yet the months went by and nothing ominous happened. Whenever I came across Cedric he appeared relaxed and cheerful, a mood that I had never seen him in before. I had previously visited his house only on those rare occasions when Elizabeth asked me to one of her excruciating afternoon teas, but shortly after Sarah moved in I received an invitation to dinner which I accepted with alacrity. There were six of us, a friend of Cedric's and two of Sarah's, and, improbable as it might seem, the mixture worked. There was a handsome young motor mechanic who set the tone by flirting with a lively academic lady who had once been a pupil of Cedric's, and a blonde blue-eyed hairdresser who flirted with me. Sarah had put together an imaginative meal, embellished with Mediterranean flourishes, and Cedric had chosen a good wine to stoke us up. They hadn't made many alterations to the interior of the house, but the insipid prints of English country life that used to decorate the walls had been replaced by brilliant posters of the Cote d' Azur. Sarah's role remained ambiguous.

It was not yet clear, at least not to me, whether she was still no more than Cedric's house keeper or whether she had now achieved the status of a *maîtresse attitrée*. I rather hoped, for his sake, it was the latter. But my hopes were not shared by his neighbours. One of them complained to me that Sarah and her friends lowered the tone of the neighbourhood, especially when they brought her home in a taxi at four or five o'clock in the morning, full of the *joie de vivre*. What's more, it was rumoured that she took drugs, and we all know, don't we, where that leads. In the confrontation between the rebellious Sarah and the self-appointed guardians of public propriety, my sympathies were, needless to say, firmly on the side of rebellion. Cedric raised the matter with me one day when I came upon him in his garden. "What is it to me, or to anyone else, if she smokes a bit of pot now and again?" he asked. "And why shouldn't she go out on a spree from time to time? Do they imagine that this street can provide all that a young person needs in the way of night life? Sarah is one of the most generous people I've ever met, and it wouldn't do those busybodies any harm if some of the generosity rubbed off on them." I thought it very unlikely that that would happen, but what did happen was that Sarah somehow succeeded in transfusing some of her vitality into Cedric. He began to take an interest in all sorts of things that had never found a place in the narrow scholarly world in which he had previously quarantined himself. There's a small football field about half a mile from my house, and I could hardly believe my eyes when I passed by one evening and saw Cedric in his anorak and trainers and Sarah in a bright red tracksuit standing on the sideline and shouting their heads off in support of the local team. But it wasn't all one way. For some of Cedric's orderliness and stability slowly percolated into Sarah's daily life. And whatever his neighbours might have thought, I knew for certain that Sarah was now devoted to the care of Cedric and his home. The psychoanalysts would no doubt say that she had at last found a substitute for her lost father, but, of course, I don't believe what the psychoanalysts say.

I thought I was beyond being surprised by anything that Cedric might now do, but I was wrong. One day, by chance, I caught sight of him going into the university library, something I was sure he hadn't done, not even once, since he retired. A few days later I saw him there again, at about the same time, and then it dawned on me that he had become a regular visitor and that, against all the odds, he had embarked on some new academic venture. When next the opportunity arose, I tackled him about this and although he was at first reluctant to give anything away, he finally confessed: "I thought I might try to write a simple little book about village life in medieval England, something that Sarah might read and enjoy." So, for the best part of a year, he spent his mornings in the library and distilled his thoughts into prose later in the day. For some obtuse reason, our university press was not interested in the finished product, which turned out to be a piece of good fortune for Cedric, for the commercial publisher who did take the book on went to a good deal of trouble to promote it. He managed to have it discussed on one of the book programmes on television, where the pundits made great play of the fact that an aged pedant had somehow succeeded in writing a book that ordinary people could read with pleasure.

How well a book sells is not nowadays determined by its quality; it is determined by marketing. That's why it sometimes happens that an unreadable book, or one that could not possibly be understood by the general public, becomes a bestseller. Often it is the personality of the author that is exploited to make the commercial killing, and to some extent that happened to Cedric too. He didn't quite become a television celebrity, but one of the Sunday papers gave him the best part of a whole page, and there was an echo of it in the New York Times. The portrait they painted was quite out of date. He came through as a shy, scholarly recluse (he was never quite that) who had been secretly harbouring this great book all his life, but had to rise above the petty preoccupations of academic life before he could write it. Cedric managed to keep Sarah out of the newspapers and gave the journalists no inkling of the Indian summer that had transformed him. The searchlight on his personality helped to attract public attention, but, after that, the book made its own way. It did not soar into the bestseller lists like a lark and then plummet down; it climbed slowly to a high plateau and stayed there. Large numbers of people must have read it with pleasure and passed the good news on by word of mouth. It was indeed a delightful book, with the impeccable scholarship worn so lightly that you were never conscious of it, and the prose so simple that it read like a fairy tale. And running through it all there was a magic thread that only a few of us could recognise: what Cedric had written was, of course, his version of a love poem.

As the royalties rolled in, Cedric found himself able to do some of the things that a modest academic pension would not have run to. Of these the one that gave him greatest pleasure was the opportunity to indulge his long pent-up desire to see more of the world. They did not at once rush to the exotic pleasure-domes of the tourist brochures, but, at Sarah's insistence, undertook a number of quiet journeys through the medieval towns and villages of France and Germany. Cedric had bought Sarah a good camera and after each of their first three trips I was asked over to see their slides. Cedric's running commentaries were, of course, monuments of erudition, but it was Sarah who had a more sensitive eye to the beauty of what they saw. Their first trip was to the albigensian country in the south west of France. They had flown to Toulouse where Sarah managed to produce some excellent impressions of Saint-Sernin, the marvellous romanesque structure that houses the relics of more saints than any other church in Christendom. There they hired a small car and drove through Cahors to Saint-Cirq Lapopie, where they spent the night in the tiny hotel on the hill. Sarah (in agreement with the guidebooks) thought Saint-Cirq the most beautiful village she had ever seen. From there they made their way to the ancient hilltop town of Cordes and on down to Albi, where Sarah succeeded in capturing the defiant mood of the great brick cathedral with remarkable fidelity. They went over Carcassonne with a fine-tooth comb and reached the sea at Narbonne. The second journey took in some of the celebrated medieval towns of south Germany. In a brand new Volkswagen that they picked up at Frankfurt airport, they dawdled through the Odenwald and the Tauber valley to Rothenburg, stopping as long as they pleased at each of the delightful old towns along the way. Then they doubled back to Creglingen to see the great Riemenschneider altar, chose minor roads to Augsberg, and ended up in the Bavarian alps at a small hotel where they could look out across the valley to the turreted splendour of Neuschwanstein. In December of that same year they flew to the Caribbean which, apart from the tropical vegetation, they didn't much like, and in the following summer they spent a month in the forests of Scandinavia. I had no doubt that the months that followed the publication of Cedric's book were the happiest in his life and perhaps also in Sarah's; but there's a worm at the heart of present happiness and I couldn't help wondering how long this idyll could last.

I expected that, sooner or later, some young man would come along and take Sarah away, or perhaps she would leave of her own accord simply because, in the long run, domestic stability and foreign travel couldn't give her all she wanted from life. But the end didn't come in that way at all. Cedric and I met in the local supermarket one morning and it struck me that he had lost quite a lot of weight. He didn't have too much to spare at the best of times, but now he looked positively gaunt. Of course, I made no allusion to the change in his appearance, but as we hadn't seen each other for a while I asked in the casual way that doesn't normally require a serious answer, if he was well. He made a point of telling me that he'd never felt better, but I had the strong feeling that he was whistling in the dark.

I didn't see him again for a month or so, and then I had a telephone call from Sarah asking whether I could spare her a few minutes to have a word about Cedric's health. It transpired that he had virtually stopped eating, was exhausted by the least effort, and appeared to be in pain, although he never made any mention of it. He didn't want to see a doctor, and Sarah was at a loss to know what to do. She thought it just possible that if I added my voice to hers, he might agree to seek the medical attention that was obviously necessary. I found him lying on a sofa in his living room and saw at a glance that there wasn't too much that doctors could do for him. The loss of tissue had produced loose folds about his neck and his eyes had sunk deeply into their sockets. There was a sallowness about his skin that I thought verged on jaundice. I did, in the end, manage to persuade him to call in a doctor, for he was going to need relief, even if there was no medication that could much affect the outcome. He also agreed, but only for our sake, to go into hospital for a day or two to have the necessary tests done, though the whole experience was something of a formality. It came as no surprise that the tumour was inoperable and that he had secondary deposits in the liver. Sarah decided there and then that he was going to spend his last days in his own home and that she would look after him, however difficult the task became. And it became very difficult. He lingered on for many weeks and eventually became a round-the-clock nursing problem, but Sarah, often half drunk with fatigue, was always there to do what had to be done. She told me that he died peacefully.

Although Cedric did leave a will, he left no instructions for his funeral and had not apparently said anything to Sarah about it either. But she decided that it was right that he should be buried beside his wife in the plot that had been reserved for him, and I helped her make the arrangements. A surprisingly large number of his former colleagues came to the burial, and one of them made a simple, deeply moving, oration. Sarah behaved with great dignity. In one respect Cedric timed his death very well. No dictators, international brigands, or rock stars died that day, so the national newspapers gave Cedric's obituary notices quite a lot of space. I don't suppose he would have found any space at all if it weren't for the popularity of the book he wrote for Sarah, but, as one of the obituarists put it, it isn't given to every academic to write a great book.

The will left everything to Sarah, which, in my view, was as it should be. But her neighbours, who had never quite accepted her presence, did not see it that way. I think I might well have been the only person nearby who had much to do with her after Cedric died. She stayed on in the house, keeping it just as it was when he died, and, on my evening walks, I would exchange a few words with her if I caught her in the front garden, just as I used to do with Cedric. She did ask me over for coffee once or twice, but Cedric's absence made these occasions too forlorn to be often repeated. Her life must have been intensely lonely, for she did not seem able to take up again with the friends she had known before she came to work for Cedric. Still, however great the change in her, I couldn't believe that she had become the sort of woman who would spend the rest of her life tending his shrine. So I wasn't too surprised when an estate agent's signboard appeared on the front of her house announcing that it was for sale. When I asked her where she intended to go, she told me that she was going to rent a flat in the centre of town and find some job to keep her busy. I took the liberty of suggesting that it might be more sensible for her to buy a flat with the proceeds of the sale of the house, but she said she had other plans for that money. The house didn't take long to sell, and she moved into town as she had planned. After that I rather lost touch with her. But a few months after the house had been sold there was an item in our university gazette that caught my eye. Some anonymous donor had given the university a large sum of money to endow a Cedric P. Memorial Lectureship in Medieval Studies.

I next saw Sarah when we bumped into each other in the town market. She seemed pleased to see me, and that gave me the opportunity to ask how the world had been treating her since last we met. She had taken a job in a solicitor's office, which was the last place I would have expected to find her, but she insisted that the work wasn't all that boring. "Anyhow," she added, "I can't spend the whole of my day poring over second-hand accounts of life in medieval villages, can I?" "Is there room in your day for a young man?" I asked. She paused for a moment and then, looking at me with what I took to be genuine affection, she said: "I don't think you quite understand. I never regarded myself as more than a bird of passage in Cedric's life; but in my life he can never be replaced." I put my hand on her shoulder and promised her that with the passage of time she would change her mind, but, as far as I know, she never did.

I still take a stroll after dinner on summer evenings and cast my eye over the suburban gardens. I don't know the people who now live in Cedric's house, but most of their front lawn has been turned into asphalt and on it there stands an expensive new car.

CHAPTER 12

A LETTER FROM VENICE

A few years ago there appeared in *The Times Literary Supplement* a long review of a volume of essays published to mark the 150th anniversary of the death of Giacomo Leopardi. Since my undergraduate days I have never wavered in my conviction that Leopardi was by far the most interesting of the European lyric poets of the nineteenth century, the only one of them who, besides being a great poet, was also a great scholar. So I read the review with more than casual interest and came to the conclusion that the reviewer knew what he was talking about. The volume, as is usual in such circumstances, appeared to be a mixed bag, but one of the essays was singled out for special praise. It was a study by a Contessa Elena di M. of Leopardi's relationship to women, in his life and in his poetry. This had always struck me as a quandary that called for deeper investigation, for although Leopardi wrote with great passion about the women he loved, he was an impotent, hunchbacked dwarf who, I suppose, can have had little, if any, physical contact with the objects of his adoration. A serious study of Leopardi's women was inducement enough for me to get hold of the book and I had no difficulty in sharing the reviewer's enthusiasm for the essay by Contessa Elena di M.

It appeared that my assumptions about Leopardi's love life were essentially correct: for him the body of a woman remained forever unexplored territory. But Elena di M. avoided the facile conclusion that his love poems were therefore simply a sublimation of frustrated passion. She argued, convincingly I thought, that Leopardi's relationships with women, in life as well as in poetry, were formed by literary models, and especially by Petrarch. The

166

influence of Petrarch on Leopardi is, of course, a well worn theme, but Elena di M. was able to show from a detailed analysis of his correspondence and his journal that, in his responses to women who attracted him, Leopardi not only mimicked Petrarch's reaction to Laura, he actually adopted a form of Petrarchean language to describe the experience. It was a case, not of the life generating literature, but of literature generating the life.

I happened to know that di M. was the surname of a distinguished family that in earlier centuries had provided several doges for the Venetian Republic, and in my mind I conjured up a rather romantic image of an aristocratic Italian lady who was not only a profound and sensitive scholar but who, in addition, wrote flawless English. But there was one small item in her essay that astonished me. To illustrate a point, she quoted a splendid English version of a passage from *Le Ricordanze,* and it was a miracle to me that she should know of it. For I had seen and admired it, almost half a century ago, in a magazine published by the students of the University of Sydney in Australia, and I thought it very unlikely that anyone would have bothered to republish it since. It was written by a girl with whom, as undergraduates, we were all in love. Her name was Claudia.

Let me tell you something about student life in a still half-colonial Sydney during the war years. Despite the ritual public claims made by politicians of Australian intellectual and cultural independence, Sydney, before the war, was very much a provincial British derivative. Those who know Sydney only as it is now, with its cluster of skyscrapers, its opera house, its richly polyglot population, will have difficulty in believing that in the 1930s the tallest edifice in the city was the T and G (Transport and General Insurance Company) Building that rose to a dominating height of thirteen storeys; that the city centre could easily have been mistaken for that of an English midland town in the late nineteenth century; that, in the height of summer when the temperature often rose above 100° F and the humidity almost reached saturation, businessmen went to their work in three piece suits made of durable English cloth. The ham and beef shops (there were no delicatessens), in addition to ham and corned beef, offered 'mild' or 'tasty' cheddar and sometimes English curd cheese, but no other. At Christmas, in the sweltering heat, the shop windows displayed snow scenes complete with Santa Claus

167

and reindeer; and Christmas dinner encompassed the traditional turkey and the full weight of Christmas pudding and mince pies. It was generally agreed that the best goods were those imported from England, the Mother Country, and, if you could afford them, those were what you bought. The press loyally reported what they thought was happening in the British Isles but the rest of the world got pretty short shrift. English games, notably cricket and Rugby, filled many pages in the Sunday papers. As in England, shops and offices shut on Saturday afternoon and everything was shut on Sunday. There were only two downtown nightclubs, Prince's and Romano's, that were thought, because they were expensive, to be respectable, and they closed at 1 am. Seedy student haunts like the Hayden stayed open a little longer. Nightlife presented a serious strategic problem for students, except for the handful that had, or had access to, motor cars, for public transport stopped well before midnight, and if you missed the last tram, you were in for a long walk home in the early hours of the morning.

What redeemed the city and saved it from being no more than a dull provincial backwater was the sea. The low hills that ran down to the spectacular harbour were then studded with old houses set in large gardens, and on a fine day the blue-green water was decorated with countless white sails dancing in the light. On the ocean side, the great Pacific rollers came charging in to break on the sands of half a dozen easily accessible beaches, and it was from there that the squalls would finally arrive that brought to an end the long spells of steamy weather that made up much of the Sydney summer. Sailing was for those who could afford it, but the beaches were for everyone.

This remote, tranquil, self-centred world was washed away by Pearl Harbour. American troops by the million passed through the city and abruptly initiated a transformation that continues to the present day. But the university changed much more slowly. Its outlook and its practices remained anchored in late Edwardian certainties, and it was only a decade before that a concerted attempt had been made to dismiss a professor of philosophy because he was an overt atheist. As you would expect, the war dramatically changed the composition of the student body. Students of medicine, engineering and other subjects deemed essential to the war effort were exempted from military service, and these faculties remained, as they had always been, very largely male preserves; but conscription stripped the humanities of all but a handful of men, so that the division between the sciences and the arts was also a division between men and women. The prevailing ethos was conformism. The men wore sports jackets, various shades of grey trousers and sober ties; their shoes were black or dark tan, but never made of suede, which was generally thought to indicate that the wearer was homosexual. Hairstyles rarely deviated from short back and sides with a parting on a left. The women wore bright floral dresses in summer, and in winter dresses of heavier cloth or tweedy suits. Manly games continued to be vigorously played, and outstanding sportsmen remained the university's cultural heroes just as they were elsewhere in the country. There were, it must be admitted, a few pockets of courageous dissidence but, for the most part, what was taught and how it was taught would have met the approval of the university authorities in Edinburgh in 1910. Except for the denizens of four or five denominational colleges, which housed mainly the offspring of well-to-do country families, the students and their teachers came to work each morning by tram and bus or ferry and, at the end of the day, went back the same way to their homes. Between sunset and the following morning, the university slumbered.

In this dull firmament Claudia shone like a lodestar. Her ancestors must have been a judicious mixture of the Mediterranean littoral and the forests of Scandinavia, for although her skin was a deep tan even in midwinter and her eyes dark brown, she had straight blonde hair that was bleached still further by the sun, but nothing else. Her face in repose I would not have called beautiful, but when she smiled your heart skipped a beat just as it did for most men when Ingrid Bergman first smiled at us in *Intermezzo*. Her clothes were always eye-catching, often a confection of her own, and hers was the first trouser-suit that I had clapped eyes on. She was said to be the best classicist the university had seen for a decade, but this did not stop her being a leading light in every irreverent manifestation of student exuberance. She was the star of the undergraduates' annual review and she wrote a riotously funny, but sharply satirical, column for the students' weekly paper.

I think I should only have admired her from afar had it not been for the *Decameron* (please don't jump to the conclusion that I am about to tell you a tale like that of Paolo and Francesca when they found themselves together reading about Lancelot). At that time all the Australian states imposed a system of strict puritanical censorship over what the public was permitted to read. You could not then legitimately buy *Ulysses* or *The Interpretation of Dreams,* to say nothing of *Lady Chatterley's Lover* which was to remain on the proscribed list for another two or three decades. And, incredible though it may seem, *The Decameron* was also banned. Somehow, one of the Australian publishing houses finally succeeded in obtaining permission to publish an English translation of *The Decameron,* but only in an expensive illustrated edition. I spent some of my scholarship money on the purchase of this volume, but found, to my astonishment, that one of the tales, Rustico and Alibech, was left untranslated. Needless to say, I had to find out what that story was about, and I tried to decipher it with the help of French, Latin and an Italian dictionary. That marked the beginning of my study of the Italian language. Italian was not then taught in any of the secondary schools, so the university was obliged to offer a one year crash course that brought you up to the level required for further work, if you could stand the pace. Now I can't claim that my desire to fathom the mystery of Rustico and Alibech was the only reason I had for enrolling in that crash course, but it must have provided the initial impulse.

I have often noticed that distinguished classicists seem to pick up modern languages as an almost effortless by-product of their activities, and Claudia was no exception. In addition to her Greek and Latin, she sat in on some of the lectures in French and German and, like myself, she had signed on for the crash course in Italian. So I saw her regularly and, as there were only six people in the class, we got to know each other pretty well. She was brilliant and bewitching, but I could never bring myself to ask her out, for the company she seemed to keep was daunting and, in any case, I did not then know how to drive even if I had been able to lay my hands on a motor car. For several months she was hotly pursued (with what success I do not know) by the captain of the university's Rugby team, an empire-builder who subsequently won a Rhodes scholarship. And once, in the society pages of a Sunday newspaper, I saw a photograph of her leaning against the mast of a rich young man's beautiful yacht. She didn't bother to see the crash course through to the end, but faded out about halfway through. I think that this was because she knew that once she had assimilated the basic structure of the language she could do the rest herself. I couldn't help feeling, however, that there was also a deeper reason, but what that was I had no idea. So we drifted apart, and although our paths continued to cross from time to time, we did little more than exchange a bit of gossip.

A few months after Claudia left the Italian class, I heard the devastating news that she was going to marry Peter E, one of the lecturers in the classics department. Peter was a gentle soul who for more than twenty-five years had done his best to impart an appreciation of Latin lyric poetry to the trickle of students who still thought the classics worth studying. He must then have been about fifty and we had always assumed he was a confirmed bachelor. He was a small, sprightly man, with a mop of curly grey hair, and I would have regarded his highly asymmetrical face as ugly if it had not been for the obvious kindness that radiated from it. I knew of no-one who disliked him and many who admired him, but no stretch of the imagination could have envisaged him as a plausible match for Claudia, and that she should have chosen him was incomprehensible. But they did marry, in a small private ceremony to which I was not invited, and when, after the war, academic visits to Europe again became possible, they took off for Italy where Peter had made plans to spend a sabbatical studying documents in the Vatican and elsewhere. He came back alone, and no-one dared ask him what had happened to Claudia.

I don't often get invitations to lecture in Italy but always find something to delight me there whenever I go. Padua holds a special place in my affections, not only because it is a beautiful, smiling city that somehow takes a visitor to its heart, but also because medical science has deeper roots there than anywhere else. A roll call of the men who taught or studied there would include most of the founding fathers of modern medicine. One such pioneer was Giovanni Batista Morgagni who was a professor there for fifty-six years and laid the groundwork for the discipline that we now call pathology. I find him a particular source of personal encouragement, for he was seventy-nine when he wrote his great work, and that gives me hope for the future. I was therefore not slow to accept an invitation to take part in a symposium to mark the 300th anniversary of his birth. It was to be held in the Bo, the historic university building in Padua where you can still see the pulpit from which Galileo lectured to his students and the old anatomy theatre that had been built by Fabricius da Aquapendente.

I stayed at the Toscanelli, which was within easy walking distance of the old university and a stone's throw from the Piazza della Frutta and the Piazza delle Erbe, the fruit and vegetable markets that straddle the great edifice of the Palazzo della Ragione. I liked to make a detour through the markets on my way to the university in the morning because that always made a cheerful start to the day. I must confess that I am not the most diligent of participants in symposia, and if there are bits of the programme that look rather dull I don't feel too guilt-stricken if I am moved to wander off in search of something more interesting. If there's a botanical garden in the vicinity, I always endeavour to find time to visit it, especially in Italy, for some of the Italian botanical gardens have been under continuous cultivation for centuries and contain curiosities that you will not find anywhere else. The botanical garden in Padua is the oldest in Europe. Many of the plants that are now commonplaces in our gardens were first systematically propagated there, and within the walled enclosure you can see some remarkably ancient specimen trees. I spent the latter half of one gentle, sunny afternoon there and walked back to the Toscanelli in the dusk. As I made for the lift, the girl at the reception desk called me over and handed me a letter. My name, care of the Toscanelli, was written on the small, rather expensive-looking envelope in a hand that seemed somehow familiar, but I couldn't place it. As I made my way up to my room with the still unopened envelope in my hand, Stefan Zweig's bleak novella, *Letter from an Unknown Woman*, floated up from my memory.

The envelope contained a single sheet of matching paper bearing the letterhead of the Contessa Elena di M. Since I still have the letter, I can reproduce it exactly:

"Dear Henry,
Speech after long silence. There was a piece about the Morgagni symposium in our local paper last week, and your name appeared among the overseas celebrities who

172

were participating. I made some enquiries and feel sure that you must be the Henry Harris who took an introductory course in Italian at Sydney University some forty years ago and who subsequently made his career at Oxford. If you are not, please ignore this letter. If you are, you may remember me, and I am writing to let you know that it would give me great pleasure to see you again if that can be arranged. I have lived in Venice more or less continuously since I left Australia shortly after the war, and as overseas visitors to Padua usually come and go via the Marco Polo airport in Venice, it seemed possible that you might be able to spare an hour or two on your way home. If so, and if the idea appeals to you, we could meet and talk of days gone by. You can reach me on the above number almost any evening and we could then decide on time and place.

Yours ever,

Claudia G."

I have always found it perilous to summon up the past and to see, with dismay, what time has done to faces remembered only in their youth. It is better to leave pleasant memories intact than have them displaced by the harsh lineaments of reality. But in Claudia's case, there was, of course, no chance that I could resist the temptation to see her again. Indeed, as soon as I had read her letter, I made up my mind to curtail my stay in Padua and give myself at least an afternoon in Venice before my flight took off for home. I rang the number on the notepaper that evening and asked for the Contessa Elena di M. A woman's voice, in what seemed to me to be native Italian, answered that it was Elena di M. speaking. I asked, a little hesitantly, whether Elena di M. could possibly be Claudia G. There was a gurgle of Mediterranean delight and the voice at once switched to English, but English in which I could still hear the traces of Australia.

"Henry! How wonderful! Can you possibly make it?"

"Of course, I can make it. Did you imagine that I might let the chance to see you again go by because of my pious devotion to Morgagni?" (Another Mediterranean gurgle.) "I'm cutting my stay here short and plan to arrive in Venice by train the day after tomorrow. If there are no unforeseen delays I should be in the centre of the city by two o'clock. My plane doesn't leave for London until the following morning. Where shall we meet? The Florian?"

"No, no, not the Florian! Not the Piazza San Marco. Not anywhere along the Grand Canal. All those places are so crowded that you can't hear yourself speak for the din. Do you know the Scuola di San Giorgio degli Schiavoni?" (I said I did.) "We could meet there at, say, three o'clock, and if you are delayed, I shall at least have the consolation of waiting for you in the most beautiful room in Venice. And we can have dinner, if you like, at a quiet little place where I am something of a regular. How does that sound?"

"Sounds wonderful. The Scuola di San Giorgio then, at three o'clock. And, Claudia, thank you for writing to me."

Claudia might well have been right about San Giorgo degli Schiavoni. Of all the cities of Europe Venice has been the most exhaustively painted, photographed, filmed, and written about. Even those who have never been there are familiar with its great vistas. When, for the first time, you look out from the Riva degli Schiavoni or the banks of the Grand Canal, your reaction is not one of amazement or admiration, but a sense of having seen it before. And when you have dutifully made your way around the tourist circuit, the impression you are left with is the sheer magnificence of it all – the ostentatious display of wealth and power, not only in the palazzi but even in the churches. The Scuola di San Giorgio degli Schiavoni is different. It is a modest functional building built by the Escalonian merchants in the 15th century in what is now a rather obscure back street, and you could easily pass it by without noticing that it was there. But as soon as you enter your eye catches the vivid colours of the paintings that completely cover its walls, paintings that some of the guide books describe as the finest collection in Venice. For once, I agree with them. Almost all of them are by Carpaccio, and they depict events in the lives of the patron saints of what is now known as Dalmatia, George, Jerome, and Tryphon. There are paintings by Carpaccio scattered all over Venice, but none more beautiful than these. They give the place a subdued and innocent sanctity that is hard to find elsewhere in the city. I managed to locate a vacant room in a modest hotel not far away, and when I had dumped my bag there I scurried off. I wanted to get to the

Scuola di San Giorgio before Claudia, so that I could see her enter before she saw me.

She came in rather hesitantly, casting her eyes about her to see if I was there and perhaps wondering whether she would recognize me if I was. I did not have the slightest difficulty in recognising her. The stark blond hair was now almost white, but she wore it as she always had so that it now formed a silver frame around her dark face. It pleased me at once to see that, as in her youth, she made no attempt to tamper with its colour. She was wearing an elegant suit made of a variegated purplish cloth that was set off by bright gold buttons, and about her neck she had wrapped a matching purple and gold scarf. She had, mercifully, not put on weight and could have been an advertisement for some Italian fashion house but for the rather worn black raincoat that she had thrown over her shoulders in the modish way that French and Italian women manage to achieve more easily than their English-speaking counterparts. Her face was a surprise. I had expected to see perhaps contentment or at least a refined composure, but the lines about her eyes and mouth could only have been put there by unhappiness or pain. There were very few other people in the room, so it took only a moment for her eyes to settle on me. Then she smiled, and the universe lit up as it had always done. She came towards me with her hands stretched out in front of her, took mine in hers and then stepped back a pace to look me over.

"Henry" she chimed "you haven't changed a bit!"

Given that my hair had gone with the wind and my temples were grey, that seemed a highly implausible assessment, but, at another level, the flattery was not necessarily insincere, and I had no inhibitions about returning it. However, as we sat down to decide what we would do with the afternoon, we were not really at ease with each other: too much water had passed under too many bridges, and neither of us was at all sure of what the other had become. The trouble was that both of us were now a far cry from being the companionable Australians we had grown up with; they would have taken a sentimental reunion like this in their stride.

I suggested a stroll through the less crowded streets and canals of the back blocks, but Claudia was obviously aching to get out of the city.

"Do you know the cathedral on Torcello?" she asked.

I replied that I knew about it and that there was even a clumsy replica of it in one of the mean streets at the edge of our town, but I hadn't actually been there.

"Then we must go to Torcello" she said. "Santa Maria Assunta is the most ancient of our churches, and the madonna there may well be the finest mosaic that Byzantium ever produced. I know a boatman who will take us to Torcello for a fair price, and then we won't have to stop off at Murano and Burano as all the tourist boats do."

As we made our way to the landing stages in front of the Danieli, I told her a little about the life I led and about my family, although I was surprised to find that she had already gleaned a good deal of information about me. The man that Claudia referred to as a boatman turned out to own an assortment of different vessels, and he let us have a small motor boat and an old salt to go with it. The sky was rather overcast, and I feared that the weather might force us into the cabin where our conversation would be inhibited by the presence of our sailor at the steering wheel. But we had barely cleared the jetty when the clouds began to dissipate, and the waters of the lagoon came to light with reflected sunlight. So we were able to sit out in the open, watch the city disappear behind us and go on talking about our complicated expatriate lives.

Hers was decidedly more complicated than mine. She and Peter had made the long sea voyage to Europe in one of the Flotta Lauro ships that plied between Sydney and Genoa, so that they were immersed in the Italian language even before they left Sydney harbour. It took them the best part of a month to reach Genoa, and Claudia claimed that by the end of that time she was able to have a relaxed conversation in Italian with the ship's officers, if not with the crew. In Rome they found a small, affordable apartment less than half an hour's walk from the Vatican. It was on the third floor of a dispiriting tenement block that had no lift, and Claudia was soon to learn the difference between the domestic amenities of the old world and those of the new. Their daily life had something in common with the honeymoon of Casaubon and Dorothea, although I think that Peter was incapable of cruelty and Claudia was much too intelligent to be bored in Rome. But each day Peter would go off to the archives and Claudia, who had not defined a specific academic programme for herself, filled in the vacant hours between breakfast and dinner exploring the inexhaustible treasures of the ancient city.

After a few weeks, however, she tired of this, and since Peter's grant was far from generous, she found a job teaching English in a small convent school close to where they lived. I asked no questions about her marriage to Peter, but she seemed to feel the need to tell me about it. She assured me that he was a kind and generous man (which I had never doubted), but she had apparently come to have second thoughts about the marriage even before they left Australia. As she herself put it, what she had hoped to find was a husband, but what she had found was a father. That was not a trivial acquisition, but it was not enough. She was already contemplating the possibility of leaving Peter and was in a rather reckless frame of mind when she first set eyes on the Conte di M. Maria di M., the count's daughter, was an attractive ten-year-old who enlivened Claudia's English classes. Teacher and pupil had hit it off very well, and it was Maria who made a point of introducing Claudia, the exotic young Australian, to her father when, as happened once in a way, he came to the school at the end of the day. To begin with, Claudia did not give the count a moment's thought.

When we reached Torcello and tied up at the landing stage, Claudia changed the subject. It was a short walk from the jetty to the cathedral along an untidy path that ran beside a canal, and Claudia, no doubt as an introduction to what I was about to see, decided to talk about Venice. Because she had chosen the Scuola di San Giorgio as our meeting place, it came as no surprise that, like myself, she treasured the relics that antedated the power and glory of the Serenissima, and what I was about to see was first built in an age that long antedated the foundation of the city of Venice itself. The cathedral, almost a thousand years old, does not announce itself with a dramatic gesture, but comes into view rather shyly from behind the smaller church of Santa Fosca. The drama is within. I have always had some difficulty in coming to terms with the heavy gold-encrusted ornamentation that forms so prominent a feature of certain traditions in Byzantine sacred art; and it was not until I had seen the madonna in the apse of the cathedral in Torcello that I began to see what it was all about. The huge mosaic on its ground of lustrous gold towered radiantly over us, not only offering salvation, but trailing clouds of glory. It was almost as if the glow of the halo had expanded to envelop the whole congregation. Here was magnificence without ostentation, and it was impossible to be unmoved by it.

On the way back to the boat we were both rather lost in our thoughts and did not have much to say to each other, but as we chugged off into a misty sunset Claudia took up her narrative again.

"I did not become involved with Vittorio di M. until after I had left Peter and was making do in a room of my own" she said, and went on to explain that it was Maria who had brought her the invitation to dine at their home. She had by then learnt that Italy was full of minor aristocrats who had little left but their name, so she was not too surprised to find that the home was a modest apartment in a decent, but not affluent, part of the city. Vittorio and Maria lived with an old body who served as cook, housekeeper and general factotum. Claudia learned later that the first contessa had been killed by a stray bomb in the last days of the war in Italy. Vittorio was in his mid-thirties when Claudia met him, not at all the dashing Latin lover, but a rather shy, dedicated historian who had written a standard work on the Risorgimento. Claudia was certainly not swept off her feet by him, but as their friendship, encouraged by Maria, deepened, she began to see qualities in him that she had rarely seen before; and when, finally, it was suggested that she might move into the spare room in their apartment, she couldn't think of any overriding reason why she shouldn't.

Her life as Vittorio's companion and, after her divorce, as his wife had not been easy. She was never accepted as a legitimate wife by most members of his conservative Catholic family, and Maria, who had initially been the most enthusiastic of matchmakers, soon came to resent the new situation in which she had to share her father's affection with someone else. This resentment was made much worse by the arrival of Claudia's only child, and although Claudia and Vittorio bent over backwards to shower affection on her, they could not prevent Maria from becoming a rebellious teenager or stop her making a premature and disastrous marriage.

"In the tradition of Vittorio's family" she went on, "our son was given a string of Christian names, but we always used the one I chose."

"And what was that?" I chipped in, seeing that it was expected of me.

"Enrico" she said musically, and then laughed. I laughed back but quickly moved on:

"And how did you come by Elena?"

"Well, you see, I have three given names, Claudia, Katherine and Helen. Vittorio decided on Elena because there were too many Claudias in his family. And that's how Claudia G. was turned into Elena di M."

I told her that I had read her excellent article on Leopardi's women and had been amazed that an aristocratic Italian lady should have known about an English translation of *Le Ricordanze* that had appeared in an Australian undergraduate magazine some forty years earlier. She laughed again and then, in reply to my query, explained how it had come about that she now lived in Venice. While they were still in Rome, a chair in modern Italian history fell vacant in Venice, and in the *concorso* that ensued Vittorio was, to his own great surprise, successful. Claudia claimed that, in the complex academic politics that determined professorial appointments in Italy, Vittorio's ancient Venetian name did him no harm. So they moved to Venice and managed to find a suitable apartment in the city centre, but far enough away from the tourist circuit to be tolerable. Claudia never managed to obtain a formal academic appointment at the university, but she did give occasional seminars there in what was classified as comparative literature, and she liked to think that over the years she did succeed in scraping together a modest scholarly reputation.

Vittorio died a few months after he retired from his chair, which was now almost ten years ago, and she had been obliged to move to a more modest apartment in the rather drab area close to the Ghetto Nuovo. And that was where she still lived, alone. I could not help wondering whether the frayed raincoat that she wore over her shoulders and that I had taken to be an element of aristocratic style might not be the product of necessity, and whether the elegant suit might not be the one she kept for special occasions.

"And what about Enrico?" I asked.

"Enrico was not an academic child" she replied, in a way that gave me to understand that there was more to it than that. "He has a small bicycle shop in Mestre where he lives with a girlfriend who, unfortunately, doesn't much care for me. So I don't see much of him."

The restaurant that Claudia had chosen was close by San Stefano in one of those small village centres that are dotted about the suburbs of Venice. The padrone greeted her with cries of "Ah, la Contessa, la Contessa" and guided us ceremonially to a table by a picture-window that looked out onto a canal straddled by the arch of an old stone bridge. The padrone seemed pleased to see the contessa accompanied by a signore of whom, at first sight, he approved. The meal was quite simple, but excellently prepared and served with great care. We had stopped talking about ourselves and drifted back to the friends of our student days. Claudia had lost track of them completely, but I still had some tenuous contact with a few, and Claudia was eager to hear whatever scraps of information I could give her. She didn't ask me about the great sportsmen or the scions of wealthy families who had pursued her; she wanted to know about the studious, and in some cases quirky, young men who then looked as if they might have it in them to forge a new intellectual life in Australia. It was as if a centrifuge had dispersed them to the four corners of the earth. One, a journalist, lived with a Japanese wife in Kyoto; another was an eminent professor of physics in New York; another was struggling to keep a small independent publishing house going in London. In the days when Claudia and I were undergraduates in Sydney, you had to go abroad if you had anything in the way of academic ambitions, and the chances were that you wouldn't come back. When we had finally exhausted our nostalgia, I plucked up my courage and asked Claudia a question that I thought she might not want to answer, but it was the one that seemed to me to hold the key to her whole life.

"Tell me, Claudia, why did you marry Peter F.?"

There was a long pause, as if she were making up her mind whether to give me an answer or not, and then, with a shrug of her shoulders, she came out with it:

"Because the man I wanted to marry was not interested in me."

"I find that hard to believe" I replied. "We were all in love with you."

"All of you? Were you in love with me, Henry?"

"Yes, of course."

She looked down at the freckles that age had scattered on the back of her slender hands:

"Why did you never let me see the slightest sign of it?"

"Because I never thought I had the slightest chance."

At that she turned away, and I did not see her face when she said:

"What a pity! What a terrible pity!"

I asked whether I could see her home, but she didn't want that.

The next morning it was raining and I decided to take a water taxi from my hotel to the airport. The boat skimmed over the lagoon in a channel that ran alongside San Michele, the burial ground of Venice, and through the drizzle I could see the dark cypresses pointing up to an unwelcoming heaven. One day, I thought, perhaps not too far away, Claudia will lie there beside Vittorio in some gloomy family crypt, a stranger in death as she had been in life, a flicker of Pacific sunlight on the moody waters of the Adriatic.

CHAPTER 13

JAZZ

I don't know whether you have ever been to Hertenstein. It is usually the first stop the ferry makes on its way across the Vierwaldstättersee from Luzern to Brunnen. At first sight there doesn't seem to be much there but the hotel, a large rectangular, featureless building set in extensive and rather overgrown gardens. It is the sort of place that you might imagine once attracted wealthy and perhaps even aristocratic patrons in the golden summers of long-gone days. Now there's an aviary in the garden with flamingoes and exotic ducks to amuse the handful of tourists who, out of curiosity, bother to interrupt their journey to Weggis or Vitznau or some other livelier place.

For reasons that are now no longer of any interest, I happened, years ago, to be staying at the old hotel for a few days and, as a resident, had access to the overgrown garden which was barred to casual visitors. If you were in the right frame of mind you could talk to ghosts there. A plaque, half covered with moss, told you that the last Habsburg king of Bohemia had lived there at the end of his life and had died there. A scattering of old-fashioned benches looked out over the lake, and it took no great stretch of imagination to see ladies in elegant Edwardian dresses admiring the sunset reflected in the water. The garden path eventually joined a little used road that led to the tip of the promontory, but the way was barred again, this time by a heavy gate bearing a notice that made it absolutely clear that the property was private and not accessible even to the residents of the hotel. Beyond the gate lay the grounds of a villa which had once been bought by Sergei Rachmaninov and, at his death, passed to his daughter Tatyana. When I was there it was still in the hands of his grandson. On the way into Weggis, if you take the lakeside road, you pass by a stone pedestal with a bronze head of Rachmaninov on it. It's none too soulful I'm afraid.

Weggis itself is a busy little resort that serves as a shopping centre for the small communities that punctuate the shores at that end of the lake. There's a colourful café close by the ferry terminal and a ski-lift nearby going all the way up to the mountain top. I had no reason for being in Weggis other than sightseeing and sat rather glumly in the café waiting for the ferry back to Hertenstein. It was not that I found Weggis depressing, far from it, but, as so often in my life, I didn't quite fit in. The town was buzzing with a jazz festival just then, and the café full of young people making an uninhibited din. I expect I must have been feeling rather envious, and I could tell from the glances they threw my way that they saw me as an oddity, an anachronism, perhaps even a different species.

One outstandingly flamboyant character kept looking my way and finally, still unsure, came over to my table. He was wearing a crimson T-shirt and fashionably tattered blue jeans, but the most striking thing about him was a mane of shoulder length red hair and a full beard to match. There was something familiar about his face, but I couldn't place him. He addressed me by a nickname I hadn't heard since schooldays, and when he saw that the puzzlement on my face was not being displaced by the light of recognition, he announced himself.

"Spud" he said "Spud Murphy."

With my imagination working hard to remove the beard and trim the mane of hair, his face gradually came into focus. Murphy had been a contemporary of mine at school, and the memory of his wayward career there, once conjured up, was still vivid. Most of the boys who made the running at that school were pretty good all-rounders, but Murphy, who got "Spud" as a matter of course, was something altogether different. He was astonishingly good at some things and absolutely hopeless, perhaps deliberately so, at others. And he was unmanageable. He rarely produced the homework that had been set, but when he deigned to turn in a piece, it was magnificent. I remember an essay he wrote on *King Lear* that was so good that it was circulated not only among the other members of the class, but, I subsequently learnt, among some of the teachers

183

too. We all knew he came from a very difficult domestic background but had only the faintest idea of what it was. He never talked about it. We knew that it must have been exceptionally bad, for he was never reprimanded by any of the teachers for failing to deliver what had been asked of him. He was often late and often away from school for two or three days at a time. If he had not been so obviously gifted, I expect that he would have been expelled without too much ado.

Spud never tired of disparaging what we were being taught. "It's not only useless" he would say "it's positively harmful." And, with appropriate expletives, he repeatedly declared his intention to leave the school just as soon as the law permitted. We were hardly the most perspicacious audience you could find but we saw through that. Regrettably, we didn't see far enough. There was one particular accomplishment that Spud had which was totally inexplicable. In the corner of the school hall there was a decrepit grand piano that we were not allowed to touch, but one lunch time, I think it was in response to a dare, Spud sat down and for a few minutes beat out some pretty good jazz. It was at the highpoint of the boogie-woogie craze and his left hand clattered up and down the keyboard as if he had been practising the art for years. How had he ever learnt to do that? It was highly unlikely that there was a piano in his house, and surely someone must have started him off even if natural talent did the rest. Although we kept prying, with varying degrees of subtlety, we never got anywhere. Almost half a century was to go by before I was given an answer to that question.

It was, nonetheless, his prowess as a jazz pianist that provided the answer to another, more immediate question. What on earth had brought this apparition to Weggis of all places? Spud was still reticent about himself, but he did grudgingly release the information that, a few years back, he had gathered together a jazz combo and although it never became a household name, it was well enough known to be asked to perform at jazz festivals around Europe and now and then even further afield. Although it had been difficult, "Spud's Crackerjacks" had managed to stay afloat in that ruthlessly commercial world and, according to Spud, they were having fun. I asked him what he had done before that, for he had left school early, as he had always threatened to do, and the best part of two decades had elapsed since then. He hesitated for a moment and then, with an acerbity that brought to mind the recalcitrant schoolboy, spat out:

"I learnt that the more interesting a job is, the less it pays."

That was all I could get out of him.

"What about you?" he parried.

"Well, it's been much as you might have expected," I confessed. "The diligent schoolboy, in an entirely predictable trajectory, became a diligent professor. It's a constricted life, but it's placid, at least most of the time. "

"And is it fun?" he asked, almost rhetorically.

"Bits of it" was all I could honestly say.

I offered him a cup of coffee or a beer, but he said he had to go, and with that he rushed off, trailed, at a distance, by two washed-out girls half his age. I took the ferry back to Hertenstein, the "Stadt Luzern". It was the flagship of the line and the vessel in which General Guizan, at the beginning of the Second World War ferried his troops into the mountainous interior of Switzerland to set up the ultimate redoubt in the event that the country was invaded.

These days most of my mail consists of unwarranted garbage, and a lot of it I throw into the waste-paper basket unopened. It's quite an event to receive a sealed plain white envelope with your address handwritten on the front of it. It makes my day if there's one like that in the post. Spud's came on a drizzly Monday morning and for a brief hour enlivened the gloom of yet one more blighted spring. It was surprising enough that he should have written to me at all. We got along well enough at school, but we were not close friends, indeed I doubt whether Spud had any close friends. I had not heard from him since our chance encounter in Weggis, and I wondered, as I slit open the envelope, what momentous occurrence had prompted this sign of life. As I scanned the pages, also handwritten, my bewilderment grew. We had both reached the age when old men bore listeners with tales of their youth, but Spud's letter contained nothing else. I could not conceive that he would have become one of the world's perennial old boys. But here was one school anecdote after another, some of them embellishments of incidents that I could remember, others news to me. And he enclosed a poor copy of a group photograph of our class in which the pair of us stood there side by side smirking. This torrent of schoolboy reminiscences was not, however, simply the outpourings of a slightly unhinged mind. It had a purpose, and it was revealed in Spud's last lines. Somehow, although I can't imagine how, Spud had heard that I was still alive and still at work, if you can call it that, in my cloistered habitat; and with wholly uncharacteristic timidity he hinted that he would like to see me again. But I knew that it was not me he wanted to see. He wanted to see the world I lived in, the world he never made.

I invited him down for lunch and suggested he come first to my laboratory where there were then three of us busily accumulating detritus. He arrived in mid-morning and, once again, was unrecognizable. The dramatic red beard had been transformed into a neatly trimmed grey hedge and the mane of hair had gone. When he removed the nautical cap he was wearing all that appeared was a benign bald head encircled by a fringe now completely white. I have no illusions about the artwork with which time has decorated my own face, but his was done with a much heavier hand, weather-beaten, I should have said, if this were not a cliché. In any case, it was not the face of a man who had spent his life poring over books. I introduced him to my colleagues who were friendly but could hardly hide their surprise that I should have an old friend who looked like that.

The cubby-hole at one end of my laboratory is just big enough to accommodate two armchairs and when we had settled into them, Spud unzipped his battered briefcase and coyly handed me a small brown paper bag.

"For you" he said.

I made the usual polite protests and then opened it, with perhaps a little more ceremony than was necessary. It contained two objects that, for me, were relics of an ancient civilization – an old school tie and an enamelled propelling pencil with the school crest embossed onto the school colours. These gifts would have confirmed my suspicion that Spud was indeed senile but for the way he said "For you." It was the emphatic stress on the "you" that suddenly turned things upside down. Spud was giving me these objects not because he was sentimental about the old school, but because he was sure I would be. Had there been something about my behaviour at school that led him to believe that I would be a faithful old boy? Or was it that my life had, in a way, been so conventional? In any case, he could not have been more mistaken. My attitude to the old school was not as uncompromising as his once had been, but it was far from devoted. The old school tie, I must admit, hangs untouched in my wardrobe, and I never use the pencil.

Spud asked the first question: "How do you manage to pass the time of day?"

"Well," I replied, after a moment's reflection, "most of my time I spend in this room putting awkward questions to the material world. I lecture to undergraduates and supervise graduates; and I sit on a few committees that I simply can't avoid."

"That sounds pretty tame" he commented and then, as he had done years before in Weggis, asked:

"Is it fun??"

My reply was a little melodramatic:

"If you make your living doing experiments, disappointment will be your daily bread. But now and again everything works and you see something nobody else has ever seen before. That, as you might put it, gives you an incomparable high."

"And do people clap when you've done that?"

"If you're lucky, you might win a few prizes or give a few lectures that some people think important. And if you like the commercial traveller's life you can try selling yourself at conferences that seem to take place weekly all over the world in more or less agreeable places."

It seemed to me that this exchange in which he asked the questions and I gave the answers had gone on long enough. We were both being insincere and we both knew it. Spud had doubtless made it his business to unearth a good deal of information about me, or he would not have written that letter. And he must have known that I was much more deeply involved in what I was doing than my practised false modesty might suggest. I paused and then changed tack:

"Spud, it's my turn to ask the questions. And don't you think we're old enough now to stop pretending." He was somewhat taken aback and shuffled his feet uneasily without saying anything, but the flicker of mockery that had been playing about his face disappeared.

"Why did you leave school in mid-stream?" I asked. "It can't have been the poverty alone. You were the brightest of us all, and for you something could have been done about the poverty."

He was slow to answer and seemed to be thinking about the matter, as if he had never done so before:

"It wasn't the poverty itself. It was what grew out of our particular poverty. My father was a drunkard and often violent. I didn't know how to handle him until I was stronger than he was. He managed to consume most of the meager income that my mother brought in. She did not have much to offer but she did her best. Doing one's best, you know, is a pretty depressing occupation. There were six children. I was the oldest. I do not think we could have stayed together if I hadn't brought in a bit of money. I won't bore you with dreary tales about how I got the money, except to say that it wasn't always a pleasant experience. And then there was Patricia. She lived in a similar house in the same street. She didn't have much above the teeth but she was, in my eyes, ineffably beautiful. She was pampered by all the adolescent boys in the street and expected to be pampered. I don't know whether my feelings for her were stronger than those of my competitors, but my determination certainly was. If I were to have any chance of getting Patricia for myself, I had to have some money to do it with. So I left school and took a job.

It was a dull affair in a pensions office where most of my time was spent helping confused people fill in forms. I was told when I was given the job that if I was diligent I might one day rise to be manager of the office. I' m afraid that prospect didn't actually dazzle me and I left, bored out of my mind, after a few months. My next job was in a bookshop where my main duty was to induce customers to buy books they didn't really want. It was quite an interesting job when there were no customers, but it paid only a pittance. Not enough, anyhow, for Patricia. Then I became an assistant to a half-illiterate, but successful, scrap metal dealer. I must have been pretty good at that for I made quite a bit of money, at least by the modest standards I was used to. Fortunately my father died a couple of years after I left school and one of my younger brothers also got a job, so that the pressure of poverty eased a little in our household. I married Patricia as soon as I was old enough, and we set up house in a couple of furnished rooms. The marriage broke up in about eighteen months, but Patricia wouldn't hear of a divorce, so I just walked out.

Luckily there were no children, although why I can't imagine."

I interrupted him at this point:

"What about the jazz, Spud? How did you learn to do that? "

He smiled, perhaps a little wistfully:

"That was one of the few kindnesses that came my way in those days. There was an old man who ran a second-hand piano shop a few blocks from where we lived. He would have been very happy to sell new pianos, but there was no-one in that area who could have afforded one. He used to buy clapped-out wrecks, do them up, and either sell them or hire them out. The shop was also his workshop so that the floor was always strewn with débris and a covering of dust. I talked him into giving me a job cleaning the place out once or twice a week. That gave me access to a piano. The old man used to be something of a pianist in his younger days and was rather pleased that I took an interest in what he was doing. Whenever I could I used to stay on a little longer to pick out some tune or other by ear. He grew rather fond of me and must have detected some kind of aptitude for he took me in hand, and it wasn't too long before I got as far as *Für Elise.* I think it was his hope that I would soon be moving on to some simple bits of Mozart, but it didn't turn out that way. I began to play simple bits of jazz instead. He didn't like that at all, but when he saw that his customers, whenever there were any, did, he let me play whatever I wanted. I wasn't too clever at reading the notes, but it seems that I was pretty good at improvising. I swept out his shop more or less regularly for well nigh three years, and when I finally stopped doing that you could say I was a budding jazz pianist.

A coincidence turned me into a professional jazzman. To get away from Patricia I found a berth as a deckhand on an old banana boat that plied between Liverpool and the Windward Islands. It was not purpose-built, but I never bothered to find out what it was used for before it was patched up to carry bananas. Near the stern there was a dingy little cabin that contained various pieces of lumber, and against one wall, beckoning me, was an old upright piano, a Broadwood. There's not much to do on a banana boat unless the weather's very bad, so I had quite a lot of time on my hands. I spent most of it banging away on the old Broadwood. I didn't have any sheet music of course, so it was all improvisation, but I had a clear memory of some of the things I'd heard Fats Waller play and I did my best to copy him. I must have crossed the Atlantic a dozen times before it occurred to me that perhaps I was good enough to be employable as a jazz pianist. The Caribbean island I liked best was St. Lucia, and it was just about then that it was opening up to the tourist trade. I talked the manager of one of the new hotels into taking me on, and my duties, which were manifold, included playing the piano in the evenings.

Perhaps it was the heat of the sun. I soon became very keen on one of the waitresses, a delightful black girl. She was thoughtful and generous, besides being very pretty, but thoughtfulness and generosity were not commodities in much demand on the island. I couldn't marry her, of course, unless I could convince Patricia to give me a divorce, which seemed highly unlikely. In St. Lucia marriage was then a rather flexible and often temporary arrangement, so it raised no eyebrows when I simply moved in with her. The two years we spent together were the happiest in my life, but in the end St. Lucia became just as boring as the banana boat. We produced a son whom we called Lucian. He bears my surname and for a while ran a music shop in Castries. I haven' t seen him since I left the island.

When I got back to this country I made a living, although not much of a living, playing jazz in restaurants and cheap nightclubs. Eventually I managed to inveigle three equally aimless characters to join me in a jazz combo. For want of imagination we called it "Spud's Crackerjacks." We didn't do badly for a few years and even made a couple of recordings, but we were eventually put out of business by the rising tide of rock and roll. We were already on the way down when you and I met in Weggis." He stopped abruptly, and it was clear to me that he didn't want to take the story any further. I suppose that, from then on, it wasn't an edifying story.

It had stopped raining, so I suggested we might walk to my college on the other side of the town. I chose the ancient alleyways and the half-hidden passages so that he could see the underbelly of the city as well as its grand vistas. It was one of those days when there was a tutorial meeting after lunch so that the buffet was a bit more elaborate than usual. When Spud saw it his reaction was consciously plebeian:

"You fellows sure do live high off the hog."

But he took very little of the food, and I noticed later that he had merely picked at it. He sat between me and a young biologist whose conversation he must have found very interesting, for I didn't get much out of him over lunch. Afterwards he chatted briefly to a couple of my friends who were intrigued but very polite, and then we set off on a guided tour of the college – the common room, the ostentatious great hall, the quadrangles and the magnificent old library. He examined it all attentively, but said little. When we had done as much as I thought reasonable, we picked up Spud's briefcase and his nautical cap and strolled over to the main gateway. There he turned, looked once more at the quadrangle with its unmade cloisters and said, with admiration rather than envy:

"It's a wonderful life, isn't it? A wonderful life."

"Yes it is" I replied and, as an afterthought, "in a way."

"But it's not for me" he quickly added, "It could never have been for me."

I thought back to the gifted boy playing jazz on the school piano, but I could find nothing better to say than "I'm not sure." He thanked me, but not effusively, shook hands and left, a solitary figure merging slowly with the crowd.

He died a painful death a few months later, and I guess he must have known his days were numbered when he wrote me that letter.

Printed in the United Kingdom
by Lightning Source UK Ltd.
131755UK00001B/381/A